A Mighty Fortress

OTHER BOOKS BY THE AUTHOR

Deep Forest

They Sought a Country

Till the Stars Appear

Tempest Over Scotland —
    The Story of John Knox

Trumpet of Salvation —
    The Story of William and Catherine Booth

Bishop on Horseback —
    The Story of Francis Asbury

Champion of Liberty —
    The Story of Roger Williams

A
MIGHTY
FORTRESS

Biography of Martin Luther

by

NORMAN E. NYGAARD

ZONDERVAN PUBLISHING HOUSE

GRAND RAPIDS, MICHIGAN

To
"BEEP" ROBERTS

1

ON the eve of the anniversary of the birth of St. Martin, the warrior bishop of Tours, on November 11th, 1483, a child was born in the humble home of a miner and his wife, Hans and Margaret Luther. In honor of the warrior saint, they named the boy Martin. Martin's parents were peasants. His father worked in a copper mine. Before her marriage, his mother had been a servant in the home of a wealthy mine-owner. The two came of sturdy stock and the child who was born to them, although very small, had a rugged constitution.

They lived in the little town of Eisleben in Saxony. It was an independent country which later was to become a part of greater Germany. In the mountains which were about eighteen miles northwest of Halle, there were great deposits of silver and copper, and in those mines Hans Luther toiled. He was a rough, crude fellow with a fiery temper, restless, ambitious, but without the education and ability to better his lot. Shortly before Martin's birth he had moved in some haste from Mohra to Eisleben.

"I killed a man," Hans confessed to his wife. "It happened in the Blue Boar tavern. When I passed the chair in which the fellow was sitting, he tripped me."

"Can you never curb your temper?" Margaret asked. "Ever since we were married it has been move, move, move for us, and all because you cannot control your fiery disposition."

Hans' rage broke forth again. He slapped his wife with such force that he knocked her to the floor.

"Never criticize me again," he commanded. "Now, woman, make ready to move."

She stood up with some difficulty, her body heavy with child.

A sharp retort quivered on her lips, but she did not give it voice: Hans' rage would be vented upon her if she did.

So, in the middle of the night, they piled their few belongings on a cart and moved out. Three months after they arrived in Eisleben, Martin was born. Six months later, hoping to secure a better position for himself, Hans moved once more to Mansfeld with his wife and baby. In Mansfeld he went to work at his customary task in the mines but ambitiously he sought to improve the family's situation. He saved what money he could in order to purchase the rented home in which they lived, and was resolved that they would settle here permanently.

Both of Martin's parents had an innate love of beauty along with their less desirable characteristics, and they planted and cultivated both a flower and vegetable garden. While poverty dogged their footsteps, the family did manage to eke out an existence, supplementing their purchases of food with the produce from their garden. Martin's mother made daily trips to the forest to gather, for their hearth-fire, dead branches which had broken off trees.

Martin's parents were harsh and overbearing, but it was the custom of those times to use the rod with frequency. His parents were determined, in their stubborn way, that their children should be brought up to be God-fearing and obedient. They went so far with their discipline, however, as to punish with a severity which was altogether unnecessary.

One day, when Martin was only four, he took from the table one of a number of hazelnuts which his mother had gathered in the forest. When he saw his mother's eyes on him Martin popped the nut into his mouth.

"What are you eating?" Margaret demanded.

Martin's face blanched, but he made no reply.

His mother slapped his face and the nut fell out of his mouth.

"God have mercy on us!" Margaret exclaimed. "My son is a thief!"

"I did not steal the nut," Martin protested stoutly. "Did you not pick the nuts for us to eat?"

"You did not ask for permission," she replied grimly.

Therewith she picked up a stick and belabored him so severely across his shoulders that she drew blood, but Martin accepted the punishment stoically. He would not cry out although she might beat him to death. That evening, after his father returned from work, the elder Luther also beat him, adding his own measure to the already overflowing cup of punishment.

8

If this seems unduly cruel, it would be well to remember that no one could conceive of any other kind of punishment in that era. Malefactors had to be made to understand the enormity of their sins, and punishment had to be severe. Schoolmasters beat their students daily. The whipping post was the least severe form of punishment meted out to malefactors by the courts.

According to their lights, Martin's parents were honest and God-fearing, industrious, independent. They attended mass regularly and never failed to go to confession on Friday nights so that they might be purged of their sins. They performed whatever penances the priests meted out to them, without complaint. To their way of thinking, the priest spoke for God, and whatever he prescribed for the salvation of their souls they performed.

They had the natural feeling that their children had to learn honesty, obedience, and piety in the same hard school in which they had been taught these virtues.

Children were born with frequent regularity into the Luther household, every year adding one more mouth to be fed. Hans Luther, with an ambition rare for a peasant in his time, was determined that his children should be educated. Since Martin was especially small for his age, he decided that he would have to learn some task in which physical toil would not be required. He resisted the temptation, therefore, to do with him what most miners did with their children, put them to work in the mines at the earliest age possible so that they might earn a few *pfennigs* daily.

It taxed the family resources to send their son to school, but before he was six, young Martin was enrolled in the parish school. It was taught by a hard-faced master under the supervision of the priest, and the school was situated alongside the parish church. The basic instruction in the school was religious. Reading and writing were incidental since they were necessary in the preparation of lessons. Instruction began with the Ten Commandments, the Lord's Prayer, the Beatitudes and the Creed. These were learned by memory and when the scholars were letter perfect in them they were recited to the priest.

There was more emphasis on the commandments than on the Beatitudes in the instruction since little stress was placed upon the love of God in the teaching. It was an angry God whom the master portrayed, One who was incensed at the sinful state of man and was concerned to mete out punishment to malefactors. The Lord Jesus Christ was regarded as wholly unapproachable by mortal men. Interceding for sinners were the Virgin and the saints, through the mediation of the priest.

For schoolboys, the saints were especially respected, since, with the celebration of their birthdays, holidays were proclaimed, usually accompanied by festivities and merry-making. The processions for the saints also gave a touch of pageantry to life, for the images were brought out into the streets and all participants were in gala attire.

One touch of brightness in each of the drab villages of Saxony was provided by the parish churches with their high, vaulted ceilings, their richly-colored stained glass windows, and the ministry at the altars. True, all of the services were in Latin which young Martin did not understand, but he was much impressed with the beauty of the church windows, and his eyes often strayed to them as he listened to the intoning of services by the priest.

While still very young, Martin went regularly to the priest to confess his sins, and he faithfully performed the penances which the priest would prescribe, thereafter receiving absolution. Father Anselm, Martin's boyhood priest, was a kindly man who detected a genuine piety in the youthful parishioner. Martin was especially conscious of his sinful state since his parents called his attention at frequent intervals to his many shortcomings.

Along with the teachings of the Church, Martin accepted the local superstitions concerning witches and evil spirits who dwelt in the mountains and in the depths of the forest, hiding in the high branches or hollow trunks of trees. These all had to be placated, and night was an especially dangerous time for a boy to be out-of-doors. It was then that evil creatures were abroad and howled in windows or down chimneys.

The schoolmaster was a sadist and constantly used the whip on his scholars. One morning Martin was punished no less than fifteen times for failure to recite his lessons perfectly. Despite the severity of the punishment which was constantly being meted out to him, he was able to read and write by the time he was six years of age. He then began the study of arithmetic and Latin.

Martin was the smallest boy in his class and, as a result, was the butt of the coarse jokes and persecution of larger boys. But Fritz Wilder, a lad some years his senior, took him under his wing and fended off some of the persecution which was directed at him. Fritz often accompanied Martin to school to protect him from the older boys.

10

Through it all: the persecution of the larger lads, the difficult examinations, which were both oral and written, Martin acquired a considerable fund of knowledge. Most of it, however, was unrelated to life.

"Why do we have to study Latin?" he inquired of Fritz one day. "We do not speak Latin to our comrades: we do not use it in our homes. We use it only in the classroom."

Fritz shrugged his shoulders.

"I suppose that we study it because it is the language in which the Bible is written," Fritz suggested.

"But why is the Bible not written in German?" Martin demanded. "Why are we not able to read it as we do other books?"

"The priests say that people should not read the Bible," Fritz explained. "It would give them wrong ideas about God and the Church."

"But if the Bible is the Word of God, as the priest says, why should we not be permitted to know what God says?" Martin demanded.

"That I would not know," Fritz replied. "But I do know that one should not question the word of a priest. He knows what is best for us."

Martin nodded his head. Yes, a priest knew everything. And, since his own thirst for knowledge was so great, he began to consider the idea of becoming a priest. If that was the way to knowledge, it would be the way of life, God willing, that he would go.

By the time that Martin was fourteen, he had completed all of the courses which were offered in the Mansfeld parish school.

"If he is to learn more he will have to go elsewhere for the remainder of his studies," Father Anselm explained to Hans Luther. "I would suggest that you send him to Magdeburg."

"But does he have the capacity to become a scholar?" Hans inquired.

"He does," the priest replied. "He has a bright and searching mind. He is the best scholar in our school. And, even though he is eager to explore new avenues of thought, he has accepted all of the doctrines of the Church without question. These are bad days, *Herr* Luther, bad days. It is good to have such an one as Martin who is always ready to believe that which the Church teaches."

For only a short time now Hans Luther had come to be known as "*Herr*" Luther. His ambition had driven him on and he had rented

11

a smelting furnace from the Count of Mansfeld. The man who had previously been managing it had been a careless fellow, much addicted to drink, and the count rightly assumed that the energetic Hans Luther could make the smelter pay.

Hans had even been signally honored by being elected to membership on the Town Council. And he had prudently put aside funds sufficient to pay for Martin's tuition and lodging in Magdeburg. But, despite the severity with which both his father and mother disciplined him, Martin set out with heavy heart and an early spell of homesickness for Magdeburg. He had as a traveling companion another local lad, Friedrick Landsman.

It was a long journey for two boys, only fourteen years of age, with the entire distance to be covered afoot, and Martin and his comrade took some eight days to make it, their knapsacks slung over their shoulders. Yet, despite his homesickness, Martin was glad to leave his family. Although his father evidently cared for him, he showed little genuine affection for any of his children and Martin was eager to be on his own. While Hans Luther had arranged to pay his son's tuition and lodging, he had not given him sufficient funds to pay for his meals. In order to eat, therefore, Martin had to make his own living. He discovered that many of the students went out into the streets and sang in front of the homes of well-to-do citizens of Magdeburg. Many of these people invited the students to enter their homes after they had sung and permitted them to eat with the servants in their kitchens. Others merely gave them scraps from their tables. It was a precarious way to make a living, but Luther became one of the prime favorites of the people who listened to his singing, possibly because he was still small of stature but also because he had a fine voice.

He prefaced his singing, according to custom, with a melody in Latin, *"Panem propter Deum,"* (Bread, for God's sake), and he learned to know in which homes there would be the greatest likelihood of securing food. This method of obtaining meals was not, at that time, regarded as demeaning. Not only students, but also begging friars from various of the mendicant orders secured their meals in that way.

On the third day of his stay in Magdeburg, Martin and two comrades encountered a monk, gaunt and gray, his cadaverous cheeks and emaciated appearance giving mute evidence of his pitiful estate.

12

"What a scarecrow!" Martin remarked to one of his fellow singers.

"But a man of noble birth," his friend told him.

Incredulously Martin exclaimed, "Do you really mean that?"

"I do," his friend replied. "He is the prince of Anhalt. He was a man of great wealth, but he gave all of his possessions to the poor and to the Church and became a friar, begging for food for himself, for his monastery and for the poor and hungry."

Martin scrutinized the man closely. Despite his threadbare condition, his garb worn and tattered, Martin realized that there was nobility and dignity in the man's appearance; and there was about him a serenity which was almost startling. Martin had collected part of a loaf of bread and several thick slices of cold meat which he had dropped into his sack to be eaten later. Impulsively he walked over to the mendicant and put his food into the man's bowl.

The prince's face lighted with a warm and grateful smile.

"May God bless you, my son!" the mendicant said.

Martin's heart held a warm glow. He might go hungry that night himself unless he could find a family who would supply him with more, but he felt that he had been amply rewarded in the glance which the friar had bestowed upon him. Boy that he was, he had a feeling that that which the prince was, was what he also wanted to be. Most lads of his age would have been repelled by the sight of the hungry friar and stirred only by the appearance of a bold knight in gleaming armor: Martin was moved, instead, at the sight of the simple but noble friar who had disposed of all his worldly goods to become among the least of men.

Many times during the year that Martin was in Magdeburg he was hungry, although on the whole he fared rather well. On occasion he might miss as many as two meals in succession, but he could ordinarily make up for the lack within the course of the following day. The fact that he spent so much time out-of-doors and took so many long walks daily helped to build up his physique and gave him rosy cheeks and sturdy muscles.

The school in Magdeburg, although it was more advanced than the one in Mansfeld, was no better as far as the attitude of the masters toward their students was concerned. There was the same discipline, the same contempt of the masters for the students, but Martin was eager in his desire to learn and made remarkable progress in his studies and especially in his mastery of Latin. He

13

also studied the Greek classics and became thoroughly familiar with the lives of the saints.

He was an independent scholar and had very profound likes and dislikes as far as the classics were concerned. As yet he did not know why he felt as he did, but his favorite Latin author was Cicero, and he early developed a contempt for the teachings of Aristotle.

A year passed in Magdeburg and then, at the urging of his mother, Martin set out for another school. Martin's mother had a distant relative in Eisenach which was twenty-five miles distant from Magdeburg and that much farther from his home in Mansfeld. But Margaret felt that if he would move on to Eisenach, her cousin would probably be willing to provide food for her son and he would not have to spend the many hours which he did in Magdeburg, singing for his meals. Margaret Luther had been born in Eisenach and felt certain that if her son would go there, his situation would be bettered.

By this time Hans Luther was making a good living from his smelter but, while he was willing to pay Martin's tuition and lodging, he was not in favor of making life too easy for his son by providing him with board and lodging.

"Give a lad too much and you spoil him," he remarked sagely to Margaret.

"True," she agreed, "but Martin should spend enough time in the schoolroom to be able to secure the education which you never obtained and which you covet for your son."

"*Ja,*" he said, "but there's no reason for pampering the lad. He should be kept busy and learn that he cannot eat the bread of idleness."

If Margaret assumed that Martin would be cared for by her cousin Wilhelmina, she was due for a rude awakening. Wilhelmina gave Martin a poorer room than he had in Magdeburg and grumbled because he paid so little for it.

"Your mother would have me wait upon you hand and foot," she remarked shrewishly. "She expects me to give you the best room in my house, but that I will not do. I do not believe in coddling boys or girls."

So Martin went out onto the street again to beg for food in exchange for his singing. During the year in Magdeburg his voice had improved immensely. It was so clear and strong that he became a favorite singer among the people of Eisenach. He matricu-

14

lated in St. George's School and went through the same process of studying and singing for his meals.

He discovered that one home, the inhabitants of which were especially generous, was a stately mansion on one of the side streets, the owner of which was a *Frau* Ursula Cotta. She was attracted to him by his fine voice and his rosy, boyish cheeks, and she asked one of her servants to invite him into the house. Then, instead of setting a place for him in the kitchen, she asked him to eat with her in the stately dining room.

Martin was still small of stature and there was something especially appealing about his demeanor which attracted *Frau* Cotta, who had been recently widowed. She not only gave him a meal but a silver coin as well. After the dinner Martin sang for her, probably better than ever, for she showed so many signs of appreciation for his effort.

"Come and sing for me again," she invited, "whenever you are in this neighborhood."

Martin did not intend to take advantage of her hospitality but he was a hungry boy and two days later he was back at her home again. Then, regularly every day, he came to her home and sang for her. A week passed, a week in which Martin was well fed and more than happy. He was completely at ease when he sang for her. His tensions disappeared.

Finally, at the end of the week, *Frau* Cotta said, "Martin, it is foolish to have you leave every day after you have sung for me. Your singing gives me great joy and comfort. I should like to have you come here to live. You would have your own room and would take all your meals with me."

Warily Martin replied, "It is most kind of you, gracious *frau,* but I am sure that I could not afford to pay for a room in a home as beautiful as yours. My father pays my room rent, but I know that he does not give me enough to pay for a room in your lovely home."

Frau Cotta gave Martin a warm smile.

"Of course you can afford it," she insisted. "You would pay for your room and your meals by singing and by giving me the pleasure of your company. It is lonesome for us who have no kinfolk nearby to be shut up in a great home like this."

Martin was completely nonplussed.

"I do not know what to say," he stammered. "I cannot begin to express my gratitude. It is most generous of you."

15

"It is not generous," she replied. "You bring us joy and happiness by your presence."

Frau Cotta was a remarkable woman. She seemed to sense the hunger in Martin's heart for friendship and kind understanding, and she gave to Martin a mother's love. This was something Martin had never felt in his own home. Both his father and mother undoubtedly regarded Martin with affection, but they were parents who could not show their feelings. They presented to all of their children only a harsh exterior. This was probably typical of a peasant family of their era but it left Martin lacking the warmth of a happy family life so essential to one with his temperament.

Frau Cotta treated Martin like a beloved son. *Herr* Cotta, he learned, had been a brusk but warmhearted man. Those who knew him had admired and respected him·and enjoyed the merry twinkle in his eyes. He had been a mountain of a man. By contrast, Martin was still small of stature, although, with the good food which was served at the Cotta table, Martin began to add both weight and height to his frame.

Frau Cotta was a genial hostess ·and there were many guests and relatives who were frequently invited into the home for dinner and to hear Martin sing. However, Martin sensed her loneliness for she and *Herr* Cotta had had no children.

Without responsibility to provide food for himself, Martin was able to spend more time on his lessons. He was also fortunate in having John Trebonius for a teacher. *Herr* Trebonious had the highest regard for his calling and for the lads who were entrusted to his care. Although most teachers were accustomed to wear their caps to classes he came into the classroom bareheaded as a sign of his respect for his scholars.

"In my classrooms are doubtless some of the future leaders of our country," he explained, "great lawyers and doctors, possibly outstanding statesmen. I want to pay them the honor and respect which some day will be accorded them."

To be sure, there were a certain number of dullards in the class, students who had no interest in their studies, no aptitude for work. Martin was undoubtedly the most eager scholar whom he had, and with the stimulus of a great teacher, Martin gave his very best. All of his passion for knowledge came to the fore. He was not satisfied merely to complete a lesson assignment: he had to pursue every aspect of it.

16

"You take great joy in your studies, do you not?" Trebonius inquired of him one day.

"Yes, master, I do," Martin replied. Then he added shyly, "But, sir, you make every lesson so interesting. You bring the pages of history to life."

"I am indeed glad that you think so," *Herr* Trebonius acknowledged.

For some time after Martin moved into the Cotta home, he excused himself after every meal and the subsequent singing period, until one evening when *Frau* Cotta said, "Why do you not bring your books down to the fireplace to study, Martin? It is much warmer here than in your room."

"But will not my studying disturb you?" Martin asked.

"No, of course not," *Frau* Cotta said. "I would be happy to have you join me at the fireside: that is, if the conversation would not interrupt you in your work when guests are present."

"It would not," Martin replied earnestly. "I would be delighted to join you and I am most grateful to you, *Gnadige Frau.*"

That, then, became the pattern for his life. Whether or not guests were present Martin sprawled out on the floor in front of the fireplace. There were occasional guests but he would be so absorbed in his studies that he would not hear their conversation. Usually *Frau* Cotta would be seated in a chair busy with her needlework.

Martin spent four happy years in the Cotta home. Only on rare occasions did he go home to Mansfeld to see his parents and other members of his family. He felt an obligation to go as often as he could, but the austerity of his home life and the continued domineering ways of his parents made him feel uncomfortable when he was at home. Home to him had come to mean the Cotta domicile, and *Frau* Cotta had seemed more like a mother than had Margaret Luther.

To Martin, the four years in the Cotta residence passed all too rapidly, but now he had completed all of his courses in the Eisenach school and was ready to matriculate in the university.

2

*I*N the late spring of 1501, at the age of seventeen, Martin enrolled in the University of Erfurt. Erfurt was a city boasting a population of more than forty thousand inhabitants, and was the capital of the province of Thuringia. It was the largest center in which Martin had ever lived and he felt like any country lad who has come to a great city for the first time in his life. At the outset, he was exceedingly shy with his classmates, until he made the discovery that the majority of them also came from small towns or the countryside and were as awed by the city as he was.

Erfurt also boasted a fine cathedral which appealed to Martin as the most beautiful and imposing structure he had ever seen. He regularly attended mass in the cathedral, which was over two hundred years old, and had a number of altars erected in honor of various saints. When Martin was not busy with his studies he frequently wandered into the cathedral for the peace and quiet which it afforded.

Martin was lodged in a *pension*, which in Erfurt was called a *burse*, taking his meals there as well. Instruction at the university was founded upon the teaching methods which Aristotle had introduced. Martin was an eager student, but was more concerned with the welfare of his soul than with a secular education. Nor could he find in his studies the answer to his ever-recurring question, "What must I do to be saved?" He had no financial problems, since by this time Hans Luther was comfortably affluent. Martin was the only one of his children who was interested in securing an education and, despite his customary rigidity, the elder Luther was eager to have one of his children become a scholar, possibly for the status which it would accord Hans in Mansfeld.

18

Most students in Martin's time were careless both as to their morals and scholastic standing. Martin, on the other hand, was concerned about both. When classmates urged him to go with them to one of the many available brothels, Martin steadfastly refused to join them. He preferred to study and meticulously prepared the lessons which were assigned him. He suffered often from a depression of his spirit, deeply concerned as he was with the condition of his soul, and he prayed earnestly, both in his room or in one of the chapels of the cathedral, that he might learn what God's will was for his life.

Undoubtedly it was during his university years that the conviction came to him that he should become a candidate for the priesthood. This decision seemed to be the only answer for him to the questions regarding the condition of his soul. Because of the yearnings and questionings which he faced, he earned for himself the sobriquet of "The Philosopher," which students used alternately with another nickname which they gave him — "Musicus."

The latter came about because music was the other side of his nature. There were times, for instance, when Martin could be as boisterous as any of the undergraduates. He loved to play the lute and often did so at social gatherings, and on those occasions he could be as carefree and lively as any of his fellows.

By 1503, Martin had completed his courses for graduation, but he had studied too hard and, after completing his thesis and taking his examinations, had a serious illness, evidently a nervous breakdown. He became moody and depressed and one of his classmates called in an elderly priest to counsel with him and, if possible, to bring him cheer.

The aged cleric was a kindly man who listened patiently to young Martin's description of his spiritual symptoms and discussed with him the nature of his doubts. Martin, at this time, had a strong premonition of death and told the ecclesiastic about it. He was immensely heartened, however, when the old man said, "Take courage: you will not die at this time. God will make you to become one who will bring comfort to many other people. He lays His cross upon those whom He loves; and they who bear it patiently gain much wisdom."

This was just the counsel which Martin needed. If the priest had poked fun at his imaginary ills, Martin could not have accepted his counsel. But when he explained to the young man that suffering was essential to the development of the character of a true believer, Martin could identify his illness as something which he needed for the mortification of his soul. Young Luther also needed strict penances following his visits to the church for confession. They appealed to him as challenges given to him by God. Immensely helped by the priest's visit, Martin was well enough by graduation time to receive his degree which was granted him in 1503, two years after he had matriculated. At this time he received the degree of bachelor of arts.

His father was exceedingly proud of young Martin's achievement and readily consented to further studies. Two years later, in 1505, he was granted a degree of master of arts. The ceremony was carried through with considerable pomp and circumstance. It was preceded by a torchlight procession and after the candidates had received their degrees was followed by a magnificent festival.

Now Martin was confronted with the need to choose a vocation. After consulting with friends and professors he decided that he would go into the field of civil law. For one who had come from his humble station in life, civil law offered the best opportunity for advancement. Since he was so well-known in Erfurt by this time, he decided that he would begin his practice in that city.

First, however, he felt that he would need to pay a visit to his family. He had been away from home for a great many years and was not too well acquainted with his own brothers and sisters. None of them had more than an elementary education, so his academic degrees made considerable difference between his situation and theirs.

His father now treated him with great courtesy, and his brothers and sisters were still regarded by the elder Luther with contempt. Nothing that Martin could say would occasion a reprimand from his father although Hans Luther ordered the other members of the household about with impunity.

When one of Martin's brothers complained to his father about the evident discrimination, Hans told him, "Your brother is now a man of quality, entitled to our respect: he has two degrees from the university. He is far above all the rest of us."

Martin interrupted at this point and said, "I beg your pardon, Father, but I am not at all different. I am not changed merely because I have degrees from a university, because I have become a legal counsellor. I am the same Martin that I was before I went away to school — no better, no worse. I would much prefer that you speak to me as you do to any other member of the family.

Horrified, his father ejaculated, "*Nein!* You are now a man of distinction and quality. A master of arts is entitled to reverence and respect. That I learned years ago."

Martin realized that it would be impossible to make his father change his mind. Apparently Hans took a vicarious pride in his son's achievements. He gloried in them and took credit for the part which he had played in helping Martin reach his academic goal. On the other hand, Martin did not regard his degrees as in any sense praiseworthy. They were merely the tools with which he would be able to work.

To be sure, his field of service would be an honorable one and one which was highly regarded by the community. Yet his decision to go into civil law was one which did not make him altogether content. He felt an aptitude for the vocation but no particular call to it: it was merely a work for which his university training had prepared him, not a field to which he felt called by that which he could accomplish through it.

After visiting his parents in Mansfeld he returned to Erfurt, contemplating all of the issues of his life and still undecided in his own mind what his future should be. As well as law, he was considering the teaching profession. Yet he was not altogether convinced that he was called either to the legal field or to teaching. As he trudged along the dusty road, the sky became dark and a storm of intense violence suddenly broke. Flashes of lightning spanned the sky, accompanied by loud clashes of thunder. Martin had never before known such a storm. He felt that this cataclysm of nature must be a sign sent from God, but what did it portend?

He knelt under a tree and began to pray. The patron saint of all miners was Anne, the mother of the Virgin Mary, and instinctively he turned to her. From his childhood he had been taught to pray to a saint, asking the saint to intercede on his behalf with the Lord Jesus Christ or the Father God.

Suddenly there flashed into his mind a portrait of the Prince of Anhalt whom he had encountered begging on the roadway during Martin's school days, the man of wealth and position who had given up everything to become a monk, begging for bread for the poor and for himself, keeping barely enough for his own use in order to keep alive, giving most of what he obtained to the poor. This picture had never been erased from his mind. He could

21

remember the drawn features and yet the saintly look. The count's vocation was not one which Martin would have chosen for himself for it was one which demanded complete self-abnegation. But was it the vocation upon which God wanted him to enter?

True, there were some monasteries in which the monks fared especially well as far as physical comforts were concerned. Many monasteries were well endowed, their monks especially well fed, their lives comparatively easy: but there were others wherein the monks took vows of poverty and chastity which they observed to the letter. The concern of these monks was to help the poor, the infirm, the aged. The Prince of Anhalt was such a monk.

Martin prayed earnestly, kneeling on the cool, wet earth.

"Help me, St. Anne," Martin earnestly petitioned. "Give me a sign and if it is the Father's will and that of His blessed Son I will become a monk and dedicate my life to God's service."

The storm continued with unabated fury, but Martin's mind was at ease. Although a tree nearby came crashing down as it was struck by a searing bolt of lightning, he knew no fear. He had committed himself to the patron saint of his father's household. If St. Anne wanted to use him in the Lord's ministry she would care for him, preserve his life. If she had no use for him then might God strike him with a bolt of lightning. The decision concerning his life was in the hands of one of God's dedicated servants: she would care for him now and in eternity.

Back in Erfurt, Martin communicated to his friends the decision which he had made. Like many intellectuals of their time, they jeered his decision and tried to persuade him that he had made a mistake.

Siegfried Dort who, like Martin, had decided on law, was very outspoken.

"This life of a monastery is for dullards," he argued. "You are a scholar, Martin. You would waste your life in a monastery. You could go far in law. It is folly to consider anything else."

"I promised St. Anne that I would become a monk," Martin replied simply.

"Did you see her?" Siegfried inquired sarcastically. "Did you talk with her? Did she answer you?"

Then Siegfried answered his own question.

"But of course you did not see her. She did not speak to you," he asserted positively. "You were fearful of the storm and you made a silly promise to a character who has been dead these many centuries."

"Her body died, as you say. Long ago it turned to dust," Martin replied simply. "But she lives and constantly intercedes for us with Jesus Christ and the Eternal God."

"You don't really believe that," Siegfried retorted. "You are too well educated to accept such an old wives' fable."

"I have promised," Martin affirmed stoutly. "I have made my decision. I will become a monk."

Other friends of Martin added their comments to Siegfried's objections. Martin was obdurate. He had made a promise to St. Anne. Through her he had made a compact with God, a promise which he, perforce, had to fulfill. The memory of the Prince of Anhalt, ragged, threadbare, a man of noble birth but truly a man of God, was ever in Martin's mind. Martin did not long for the quiet of the monastery. He had no desire to escape from the world into a monastic order; but he was eager to escape from worldly pursuits into a fellowship with men of God. He was committed.

Eventually his friends accepted his decision.

"When do you plan to enter the monastery?" Siegfried inquired one day.

"On August 17th," Martin replied. "There are a few matters to which I must first attend. Then I shall go to the monastery and, if they will have me, I plan to become a religious."

"Then we must have a party the night before you go," Siegfried announced. "If you were going to be married, we would have a gala affair before you took the vows of matrimony. Since, after becoming a monk, you will never marry, we shall have a party to celebrate your decision."

Martin smiled.

"Do that if you will," he said. "I would be delighted to attend."

"And you will sing for us?" another of his friends inquired wistfully.

"Of course."

"And play your lute?"

"If you desire."

Differing from the customary bachelor parties which young men planned for their friends on the eve of matrimony, the party for Martin was one in which drinking was held at a minimum, a few rounds of beer for the participants, but no more. They sang and joked and recalled episodes of their collegiate careers. Martin had participated in very few of them but he had been a favorite of his classmates. The party lasted until early in the morning when all but two took their departure.

Siegfried and Adolphus Schwarzfeld stayed.

Dolph remarked, "Siegfried and I decided to accompany you to the gate of the monastery. We will not enter, of course. Neither of us were cut out to be monks, but we do want to see that you enter safely."

For a moment a doubt occurred to Martin's mind.

"Perchance the prior will decide that I am not sufficiently worthy to be one either," he remarked, "but, God helping me, I shall try to measure up to their standards."

"You will," Siegfried drily assured him.

3

$\mathcal{T}$HE only possessions which Martin took with him when he entered the door of the Augustinian monastery in Erfurt were two books: the works of Plautus, the great Roman comic dramatist; and Virgil, whose poetry had made a lasting impression upon the mind of the young Luther. He left everything else behind.

The monastery which Martin entered was that of the Brothers of the German Congregation of the Order of Hermits, familiarly called Augustinians. The order had been founded in the twelfth century and its rule had been based on the teachings of Augustine, an early Church Father and one of its leading theologians, who had lived in the fourth century and whose writings still dominate the thinking of the Church.

After Martin had been admitted to the monastery, he had several long conferences with the prior. These were concerned with Martin's religious experience, his reasons for assuming that he had received a call to lead the monastic life, and the background of his spiritual preparation. The Augustinians had applicants for membership from men who had left many different walks of life: scholars, peasants with little or no education, professional men. Only bachelors or childless widowers, of course, could be accepted into the ranks of the order.

The Augustinians were concerned to know whether or not candidates would be amenable to discipline and whether they sought entrance to escape toil and find security, or were interested in making a contribution to the welfare of the monastery and the poor whom the monks served.

After several conferences, the prior was completely satisfied with Martin's explanation of his call. He was especially impressed with Martin's account of the storm. To the prior this was certain evidence that he had received a call to holy orders. However, no one was accepted into the order without passing through a year's noviate.

On the evening following Martin's final conference with the prior, he was led to the chapel and, during the evening service, was officially received into the order as a noviate.

Gravely the prior intoned the words, "We receive you on probation for one year, and may God, who hath begun a good work in you, carry it on to perfection."

During the service, Martin was on his knees, and the other brethren, kneeling before the altar, chanted, "Amen!" as Martin became a probationer of the order.

Immediately after this portion of the ceremony was concluded, one of the older monks motioned to Martin to rise and then placed over the latter's head the white tunic with mantle and hood with which Martin was then vested. Over this garment was placed a serge slip, fashioned like a sleeveless, open pinafore, which was known as a scalpular. Thus robed, Martin knelt once more as the prior said, "Who hath converted this young man from the world, and prepared him for a mansion in heaven, grant that his daily walk may be as becometh his calling, and that he may have cause to be thankful for this day's work."

Thereafter Martin was in seclusion for a month, a time which he spent in prayer and meditation. This was a period when, all by himself, completely free from the distractions of the world, he might re-examine his own soul to ascertain whether this had been truly a call of God to live a life of total separation from the world or had been, instead, the decision of a moment, later to be regretted. Without prejudice, Martin would have been free to depart from the monastery at the end of the month if he had so willed, but Martin completed the month's meditation more than ever convinced that God had laid His hand upon him and had called him into His ministry.

In the meantime, word had reached Hans Luther that his son had entered the monastery and had begun the religious life.

"All my years I labored hard that he might receive an education and that he might become a man of standing in the world, and how does he reward me?" he complained bitterly. "Instead of preparing for a position of eminence and honor he becomes a nameless monk."

"It is a worthy profession," his wife replied, for once taking exception to her husband's mandate. "And who knows? Martin is a fine scholar. He may even become a bishop."

"A monk become a bishop?" Hans snorted. "Bishops are not chosen from their ranks. It would be different if he were a parish priest. He might advance in such a position; but as a monk he will never occupy a position of eminence in the Church."

Since Martin was out of communication with his family and completely withdrawn from the world he knew nothing of their colloquy. He had chosen a vocation in which, for a considerable period of time, he would be out of touch with both friends and family.

After the month of seclusion had terminated, during which time he might conceivably have decided that monastic life was not for him, Martin entered the life of the monastery, and came out of the solitary seclusion which had been his lot, in order that he might meditate upon his vocation. His life was still one of seclusion which he shared with the other brothers.

From that time on, during his year's noviate, he was left to the guidance and leadership of one of the older monks, Father Abelard, for instruction. He was taught how to walk, how to hold his hands folded into his sleeves, what his manner of eating and drinking in the presence of his superiors should be, and how to speak to women.

During this period, in company with all of the brethren, he also was expected to make weekly confession of his sins. This confession was made in the presence of all other monks. In addition, he had to report publicly any lapses on the part of his brothers as they also reported on any derelictions in his conduct.

These weekly confessionals were a trial to Martin's spirit for, while he willingly and humbly confessed his own sins, some of them doubtless real and others fancied, he found it difficult to report on the delinquencies of his fellow monks. Probably it also irked him to have not only discrepancies in his conduct but his inner thoughts dissected in this public manner.

However, Martin accepted this as a part of his training and an accepted rule of the order, and he sought to make changes in his character and ways of thinking which his fellow monks apparently deemed necessary for the good of his soul. To be sure, among his colleagues were some who could see the motes in the eyes of their fellows while missing the beams in their own.

Undoubtedly Martin was also able to recognize the fact that he had one besetting sin, that of pride, coupled with impatience. He possessed a brilliant and incisive mind which was able to grasp truth quickly, sorting out the nonessentials in any given situation from principles which were basic to Christian thought, and he was frequently impatient with those whose powers of reasoning were not as keen as his own.

After each public confession it was decreed that there would be a private confession which would be made to the prior who would then prescribe what penances he would deem necessary for the good of the souls of his charges. For minor failures, such as falling asleep during chapel services, the prior might prescribe such penances as the repetition of a specified number of times for prayers or psalms; for major discrepancies there would be self-flagellation or even a period spent in fetters. Martin probably welcomed these as essentials to counteract the sin of pride.

Since Martin had had a brilliant academic career and many, if not most, of the brethren, were men with little or no educational backgrounds, penalties imposed upon him were frequently much more severe than those which were meted out to less able brethren. He performed the most menial tasks with proper humility of spirit. He also engaged in the customary tasks allotted to the brethren, such as sweeping and scrubbing the floors of the chapel and living quarters, going into town with a sack on his back to beg for alms, and other tasks common to all of the brethren.

As he trudged along the streets of Erfurt, he often met his old friends who glanced at him with pity. His former classmates often tried to give him food for which they themselves had begged, but Martin, knowing how difficult it was for them to secure provender, soon began to avoid them. They assumed that his embarrassment was occasioned by shame at being found by them in dusty sandals and threadbare garments, an altogether different man in his appearance from their friend of old. They would greet him gravely with none of the gay raillery which they had shared of old.

The two years which Martin spent in the monastery, however, were fruitful years. Martin performed all of the duties which were assigned to him with eagerness. At the same time Martin often turned to the excellent monastery library for study and refreshment of his mind and spirit. The monastery possessed a copy of the Scriptures which was available to all of the monks and he studied it with diligence. In all of the disciplines, both physical and mental, he earnestly sought to purge himself of the sins which weighed so heavily on his conscience. His basic form of penance was the enactment of good works.

The fact that he could not identify the sins for which he felt guilty, made the task especially difficult. He felt weighed down by a sense of sin and yet unable to pinpoint those discrepancies of character and conduct which made him a sinner. Like the Apostle Paul he would describe himself as "chiefest among sinners," and yet be baffled by his inability to know exactly wherein he had erred.

A number of years later, Martin described his heart-searching in these words: "If ever a monk entered into heaven by his monkish merits certainly I should have obtained an entrance there. All the monks who knew me will confirm this; and if it had lasted much longer, I should have literally become a martyr, through watchings, prayer, reading and other labors."

In spite of all his austerities, his earnest pursuit of eternal truth through his studies in the library, his menial labor, and his constant prayers, he could not find peace and happiness. The prior, who was an austere man but altogether just, sought to help him. In fact, the duties which he laid upon Martin were assigned to him in order to help him find the peace which he so earnestly sought.

After striving in vain to find an answer to Martin's spiritual problems the prior brought the young monk's situation to the attention of John Staupitz, who was vicar-general of the Augustine Hermits for all Germany.

"Perhaps Martin was too young when he joined us," the prior suggested. "Although Brother Martin comes from a peasant family, he is a brilliant scholar. Possibly his learning is one of his greatest stumbling blocks. For that reason I have given him the most humble tasks which I could find for him in the monastery. He has done them all willingly and humbly and there is no one who spends more time in his devotions than he does."

"Would you like to have me meet with him — possibly to help him — at least to ascertain what is his spiritual state?" Staupitz inquired.

"You might do much for his soul," the prior replied.

Martin was summoned to a private room and met with the vicar-general. Staupitz was a shrewd but kind-hearted man, much older than Martin. He had had his own spiritual difficulties and could understand the strain under which Martin labored.

With friendly directness he began to probe the mind of the young monk.

"Surely you have found the peace which you craved here in the monastery," he began. "What, then, are your difficulties?"

Martin spread his hands wide in a despairing gesture.

"It is in vain that I make promises to God," Martin replied. "Sin is always too strong for me."

"Look to the wounds of Jesus Christ," Staupitz suggested earnestly, "to the blood which He has shed for you. It is there where you will see the mercy of God. Instead of torturing yourself for your sins, cast yourself into the arms of your Redeemer. Trust in the righteousness of His life, and the expiation of His death."

Martin shook his head.

"But I must be changed," he objected, "before God can receive me."

"No, no," Staupitz insisted. "In order to be filled with the love of that which is good, you must be filled with the love of God. If you wish truly to be converted, seek it not in these mortifications and penances. You must love Him who first loved you."

Earnestly Staupitz prayed with and for his young monk, finally dismissing Martin with a blessing. Luther pondered Staupitz's words for a long time. He studied the Scriptures and became convinced that Staupitz had spoken words of truth. He discovered in them that which afforded him a measure of peace but he felt that his faith was still weak.

Staupitz became deeply interested in the young monk and had conferences with him whenever he visited Erfurt. In considerable measure he actually laid the foundation for Martin's later break with the Church. Staupitz gave Martin a copy of the Bible, a rare possession for an individual, whether lay or clerical, in those days when Bibles were still chained to church pulpits. Then he suggested that Martin begin to develop his way of thinking not from the teachings of the universities but from the Scriptures themselves. Martin began immediately thereafter a concentrated study of the Bible, becoming especially interested in the epistles of Paul.

Martin sensed that Staupitz had helped him immensely, and he began to find a peace of mind by earnest study of the Bible which before had been lacking. However, he had a setback when he became seriously ill, at which time all of his old doubts reappeared. Thoughts of his own sinfulness, in contrast with the holiness of God, disturbed his mind.

During his illness, he was visited by one of the oldest brothers who resided in the monastery, a white-haired, sweet-spirited old saint, who spent many hours ministering to the temporal as well as the spiritual needs of his young brother. When Martin told him about his doubts and perplexities, the old brother advised him to make a thorough study of the Apostles' Creed.

"Keep in mind especially, 'I believe in the foregiveness of sins,'" he suggested. "You must not only believe that David's or Peter's or Thomas' sins are forgiven. The commandment of God is that we believe our own sins are forgiven. To believe less than that is to fail to trust in the goodness of God. Remember, too, what St. Bernard says in his discourse on the creed. The testimony which the Holy Ghost applies to your heart is this, 'Thy sins are forgiven thee.'"

Martin began to understand not only that Jesus Christ was the sole and sufficient way to salvation, but that he had to have confidence that the Master would pardon his sins.

"If you fail to believe that you are, in effect, refusing to trust Him," the aged monk told him: "if you will believe that, then, indeed, will the Holy Ghost be able to do His good work in you and through you. Yield to Christ and you will know beyond the peradventure of a doubt that you are saved."

Martin revealed to John Staupitz the advice which the fine old monk had given him.

"He is right, you know," Staupitz said, "for he has found in his own life and experience the peace which you are seeking. Brother Peter is not a man who has been educated as you have been in the university. His education has come through communion with God."

Gradually, therefore, Martin began to find the peace of mind which he had been seeking and, at the end of two years, the prior and Staupitz decided that his noviate should come to an end and Martin should receive holy orders. He had achieved not only health of body but of mind as well.

On the second day of May, 1507, Martin Luther was ordained to the priesthood. Officiating at his ordination was Jerome, the bishop of Brandenburg. Martin's family was duly invited to attend the service but his father, disappointed in his son's choice of a vocation, refused to be present. However, a short time later, when Martin was scheduled to conduct his first mass, Hans Luther decided to attend the service in the Erfurt church. Hans was impressed by Martin's strong earnest voice as he followed the ritual of the Church.

Apparently Hans had relented somewhat, but his capitulation was not complete. He brought a generous present for his son but expressed his disapproval of Martin's step in entering the priesthood during their conversation after the service. When Martin insisted that he had done the only thing which was possible in the light of his call from God, his father voiced the further objection, "Have you not heard that a man should honor his parents?"

After he had received holy orders, Martin discovered that his lot was to be greatly changed.

"He has been tried in every way and not found wanting," John Staupitz told the prior. "Now I have an assignment for him which will utilize to the fullest extent Brother Martin's many genuine talents."

"What do you intend to do with him?" the prior inquired.

"Assign him to a professorship in the University at Wittenberg," Staupitz told him.

The University at Wittenberg was a new institution, founded by Frederick the Wise, Elector of Saxony, in 1502. Frederick hoped that the university would rival the famous school which had been founded much earlier at Leipzig. Among the professors who had been chosen for the institution were monks from the monastery at Wittenberg. Martin, therefore, was assigned to the monastery there. This was only one of a number of the houses which had been built and were maintained by the Augustinian Hermit order to which Martin belonged.

Wittenberg was a much smaller city than Erfurt. It was situated on the banks of the Elbe River. University charters were usually granted by the pope but the charter for the University of Wittenberg had been granted by the Emperor Maximilian. The little city of Wittenberg itself was unprepossessing in character and appearance. It had none of the culture of other university centers. Its people were notoriously rough, rude, boisterous, given to drunken debauchery, scarcely the most propitious location for the establishment of an institution of higher learning; but Frederick the Wise believed that such a school could lift the level of learning and culture of his people.

Most of the universities of Europe at this period based their teaching methods on the precepts of Aristotle, the Greek philosopher. Martin undoubtedly rebelled at the idea of approving the methods or lecturing on a personality in whose teaching he did not believe, but he was a man under orders, and as such he sought to explain the teachings of Aristotle according to the tradition of his times.

A short time later he was given an assignment much more to his liking. He was appointed to teach the Holy Scriptures, and in this field became a truly inspired professor. He worked far into the night in his study of both the Greek and Hebrew languages, comparing the original texts with the copy of the Latin Vulgate which John Staupitz had given to him. His first assignment was a study of the Psalms. When he completed this course he turned to the New Testament and began to expound Paul's letter to the Romans.

He was such an inspired teacher that the University of Wittenberg soon became known over the length and breadth of Germany as the school in which that dynamic monk, Martin Luther, made the Scriptures come to life. One of his students, Johann Mellerstadt said of him, "This monk will put all the doctors to the rout; he will introduce a new style of doctrine, and will reform the whole church. He builds upon the word of Christ; and no one in this world can either resist or overthrow that word, though it should be attacked by the weapons of philosophers, sophists, Scotists, Albertists and Thomists."

Because of Martin's fame, John Staupitz urged him to preach as well as teach. There was actually little preaching in the Church in Germany. Most priests were content to race through the masses and spend little time in preparing sermons. Martin shrank from preaching — not because he was not able to preach but because, as he expressed it, "It is no light thing to speak to men in God's stead." He felt that it was presumptuous on his part to inform people what their duties were and wherein they failed, for he considered himself, as has been noted, a great sinner.

Since Martin believed in obedience as a prime rule of his order, however, he went on to preach and soon became so popular that crowds flocked to hear him. His messages were warm, colloquial, based on the Scriptures. One of his fellow professors said of his preaching, "He has a lively and impetuous eloquence, which delights and captivates his audience." He was only twenty-seven years of age at the time. His fellow monks were among those who eagerly listened to him, and a Jesuit, visiting in Wittenberg had this to say about his preaching, "He acquitted himself in his various engagements so as to gain great applause, and to render himself considerable among his brethren."

From all indications, he had before him a great and useful opportunity for service to his Church and his order. He had no criticism to offer concerning the tenets of his faith. He was a loyal churchman and completely committed to the Church and its dogma.

Because of his earnestness, his devotion to the Church, and his total lack of sophistication, therefore, he was deputized by his order to go to Rome to present to the pope the point of view of his order in a conflict which had developed between the German Augustinian Hermits and the vicar-general of the pontificate, a controversy which had come about especially because of the austerity of the brethren in Germany.

Martin went on this journey accompanied by an older monk, Brother Thomas. They had been allotted ten gulden, not to pay for food and lodging for which they were expected to beg along the way, but as a fee for an advocate whom they might employ to represent the Augustinians at the court of Pope Julius II.

As they trudged along on foot they murmured their prayers. It was an interesting experience for Martin who had never left the country of his birth. He was especially impressed when they came to the Alps and saw the towering peaks. When they had crossed the Alps they came out on the beautiful Lombardy plain. There were olive groves and vineyards in abundance. The people, too, were generous and the two priests fared well as they passed down the peninsula on their way to Rome.

They made a brief halt in Milan where Martin was overawed by the sight of the beautiful cathedral. Even the monastery of their order was built of marble. Accustomed as they were to simple, elemental fare in the two monasteries where Martin and his comrade had lived, they were shocked at the sight of the rich foods which were placed before them. Bluntly Martin criticized the self-indulgence of the Italian monks, undoubtedly making himself thereby a most unpopular and unwelcome guest.

Thereafter, as they continued their journey, the two refrained from visiting any other monasteries. Instead, they ate the simple fare of the farmers, food to which they were better accustomed.

34

In Florence, the next city which they visited on their journey, Martin heard the story of the courageous Dominican monk, Savonarola. The latter was a churchman after Luther's heart for he had not hesitated to criticize the sins of the people, the corruption of the Church, and the rapacity of the wealthy. Martin also learned what Savonarola's reward had been for his attempts to reform the Church: excommunication by the pope, imprisonment and ultimately hanging and cremation.

For one who had loved and revered his Church, who had given his life to its ministry and believed in its integrity, it must have been a rude awakening. Martin probably heard of the decision of the Church as it had been communicated to the recalcitrant Dominican by the bishop of his diocese.

Divesting Savonarola of his monastic robe, the bishop had pronounced the sentence: "I separate thee from the church militant and triumphant."

"Militant," Savonarola had retorted, "but not triumphant. Triumph rests not with you."

These stories he had never heard either in Erfurt or Wittenberg. Such a view of the Church had never confronted him. He had seen in the beloved Church only absolute perfection. Nevertheless, he rejected all evidences of present-day corruption. Those who had hanged Savonarola were sinners like himself. Martin was aware of his own sinful nature. There were naturally in the Church others who were sinners. In Rome things would be different. The Holy Father would be like a saint in his character. As God's vicar upon earth he would be sinless, a true follower of the Nazarene.

Yet in Rome, too, he found not only evidences of moral decadence but impiety and infidelity. When he attended mass and followed the words of the ritual he saw and heard so much of worldliness that his soul was completely revolted.

"At Rome," he later wrote in his Journal, "I heard them say mass in such a manner that I detest them: for at the communion table I heard courtesans laugh and boast of their wickedness; and others, concerning the bread and wine of the altar, saying, 'Bread thou art, and bread thou shalt remain.'"

Martin observed the princes of the Church, the cardinals in their beautiful robes, driving about in gilded chariots, umbrellas of peacock feathers opened above their heads to keep off the sun. When he conducted mass himself, as he did on several occasions, savoring each word of the ancient litany, several attendant priests urged him to hurry.

One of the assisting priests laughingly interrupted his service, saying, "Quick! Quick! Send our lady her son back speedily."

He heard the story, current in Rome at the time, about the wealthy priest who had recently died and had left to his heirs a huge fortune. He had set down on parchment before his demise his injunction to his successors: "I extorted and oppressed as long as I was able: and while you have power get what you can."

Sick at heart, he decided that he would seek to obtain the indulgence which the pope had promised to all who, on their knees, would ascend Pilate's staircase in the chapel of Scala Santa in the Lateran. On each step he murmured the appointed words which would reduce his stay in purgatory by nine years for each step. But as he went through the formal petition there suddenly flashed into his mind the words, "The just shall live by faith." He rose from his knees and fled from the place.

Years later he said, "I would not have missed seeing Rome for a hundred thousand florins. If I did I should ever had been uneasy lest I might have done injustice to the pope."

There is no record that Martin and his brother monk were ever able to obtain an audience with the pope. They often saw him being carried through the streets of the Eternal City on a resplendent litter but the two simple monks did not possess the influence necessary to secure an audience with him, and their own brother monks in the Augustinian order either would not or could not help them.

The two finally turned away from the city. Martin was gravely disillusioned but he was still a devout Catholic. During Martin's absence from Wittenberg a new prior had been appointed as superior, his old friend and former schoolfellow, Wenceslaus Link. Martin plunged at once into his lectures at the university. He dismissed from his mind the memory of the unpleasant experiences that he had had in Rome and blotted out of his thoughts any doubts which they might have bred.

4

JOHN STAUPITZ counselled Martin early in 1511 that he should begin working on the degree of Doctor of Theology. "If you are to spend your life lecturing — for which vocation you seem to be especially well adapted — you should have this degree," he suggested.

"But if I aspire to it I will have greatly increased responsibilities outside of the precincts of our monastery and much less time for study," Martin objected.

"That is true," Staupitz agreed, "but you can be of much greater service to our order and to the Church in this field of endeavor, and a few years spent in preparation will give you the increased knowledge which you will need for the task."

"But it is incumbent upon a doctor, according to the oath of his office, to explain the Scriptures to all the world and to teach everyone," Martin replied.

"That is true," Staupitz agreed, "but you are eminently well fitted for just such an assignment." Staupitz added with what seemed almost prophetic vision, "You should submit because the Almighty has signal services to be performed by your instrumentality in the Church."

The funds which were needed for tuition and fees were provided by the Elector Frederick and in 1512 Martin received the hat and ring emblematic of his eminence in the field of theology. It was a gala occasion and old friends from Erfurt, both lay and clerical, came to Wittenberg especially to witness the conferring of the degree upon Martin.

Among the new friends which Martin made, as a result of his increased prominence and responsibility, was the theologian Spalatin, chaplain to the Elector Frederick. More and more, also, he won the esteem of the Elector who often attended his lectures. He became an avid reader of Martin's books, as one portion of the Scriptures after another was written, after first being delivered as lectures in the university and the parish church.

Martin's first published work was a commentary on the Book of Psalms which was followed by a commentary on the letter of Paul to the church at Rome. In preparation for the lectures, Martin studied the Old Testament in the original Hebrew whereas most commentators of his time based their studies on the Latin Vulgate. When commenting on the Book of Romans, Martin used his Greek Testament as his source book.

The study of the Bible was a revelation to the young monk and he learned more from his research and his teaching than he had learned as a student. Again he had cause to ponder the words of Paul, "The just shall live by faith." All of his training prior to this had been that the just lived by works of penance, charity and deeds of special merit. Now he was beginning to learn that the basis of the spiritual life was faith in God and in the Lord Jesus Christ.

Perhaps a part of his popularity was occasioned by the fact that his interpretations of the Scriptures were arrived at independently of the teachings of the Church. Such independence was frowned upon by the church leaders but it gave a freshness to his teachings which was appreciated by most of his auditors.

Philip Melancthon, who became his friend and disciple, said of his teaching some years later that "the light of a new learning had arisen after a long, dark night. All devout people were much taken with the sweetness of the doctrine, and it was welcome to the learned, as though Christ had appeared out of gloom, prison and decay."

In 1515, Luther was appointed vicar for his order and had under his jurisdiction eleven monasteries. He preached as often as possible in Wittenberg but spent much of his time visiting the monasteries which were under his charge. He made a very useful contribution to his order in this field because he had such a warm appreciation of the problems and reasons for failure in others. He had to discuss administration problems with priors and give to faint-hearted monks and noviates new faith and courage to continue in the service of the Church.

During this period, he came into the confidence of the new

Elector of Saxony, George, who had succeeded the Elector Frederick. This friendship was to stand him in good stead in subsequent years.

Because of his contempt for the teachings and methods of Aristotle, he found himself in controversy with his former tutor at Erfurt, Jodocus. In a sense this controversy was almost as significant as the one in which he would later be engaged with the Church, for he condemned thereby the educational methods of all the great universities of the continent since they based their methods of instruction as well as their philosophy upon the pronouncements of the great Greek teacher.

When Martin visited Erfurt, Jodocus refused to have any intercourse with him. Luther was exceedingly unhappy but he could not forswear his position. After he had left Erfurt to go to other centers for lectures he wrote to his former friend and tutor telling him of his deep sorrow at their estrangement but reiterating his position. In this letter was to be found a foretaste of positions which he would later assume when he took issue with the Church as well, for he pointed out that, although the Church stood in dire need of extensive reformation — a position which was held by many churchmen of the time — this reformation could never take place until the process and scope of the educational system was also changed.

Thus Martin found himself in a position in which his way of thinking, both philosophically and theologically, was in many respects contrary to the thinking of both the church and the educational leaders of his day. However, the Church allowed considerable latitude in both these fields. There was a great deal of independent thinking in the Church. Martin entered upon serious controversy with the Church only when he challenged a fundraising program which had been concocted by advisers of the pope for the purpose of completing the beautiful cathedral of St. Peter's in Rome.

Julius had died and had been succeeded by Leo X. Leo inherited his predecessor's ambition to make St. Peter's the greatest church in Christendom but there were not sufficient funds in the papal treasury to make this possible. It had long been the custom of a succession of popes to raise funds by the sale of indulgences; but never had this scheme been practiced on such a grandiose scale as Leo devised.

The plan was a remarkable commercial program whereby —

literally on a commission basis — the sale of indulgences was farmed out to leading ecclesiastics for whatever purposes they might have in mind; one-half of the total which was raised, however, would go to the pope for the completion of St. Peter's.

In Germany, the program was carried out under the direction of Albert, who was both the archbishop of Magdeburg and the Elector of Mainz. The Dominican friars, Accumboldo and John Tetzel, were commissioned to put the plan into effect. Both of these friars had unsavory reputations and were notorious for the depravity of their conduct. The name of Accumboldo has been forgotten, to be sure, but that of John Tetzel is remembered to this day. Tetzel was an especially depraved knave. Some years before he undertook the task of selling indulgences, he had been convicted of adultery and had been sentenced to be thrown into the River Inn, but he had been reprieved by the elector.

The vast majority of the members of that order would have been appalled if they had been invited to do what these two monks set out to accomplish. There were many noble members of the order who, if they had been approached, would have refused point-blank to sell indulgences just as members of Martin Luther's Augustinian Hermits would have had nothing to do with such a scheme. But Accumboldo and Tetzel were ambitious and utterly without scruples and made excellent solicitors for this nefarious method of raising money for the Church. It is also safe to say that not all of the archbishops of the Church would have gone along with the program but the archbishop of Magdeburg, although not an unlearned man, was an exceedingly covetous individual.

The two Dominican friars printed notices in which they announced that they had indulgences for sale. Tezel added, in a public proclamation, that it would be possible to obtain an indulgence even for the sin which the Church regarded as most heinous, that of violating the "mother of God" herself. Thereafter were listed many of the other sins for which indulgences could be obtained.

When Martin heard about these notices, he could not believe that they had been published. Someone must have made a mistake in announcing that this had actually come to pass. When, therefore, he obtained a copy of the indulgences, he was thoroughly shocked. His next reaction was that this must be a private venture of two unprincipled priests. Certainly it could never be sanctioned by the archbishop. Then, when he discovered that the

40

archbishop had actually authorized the program, he was confident that the Holy Father in Rome could have had no part in it.

Martin's indignation was no greater than that of the princes of Saxony who, when they heard of the shameful traffic which had been initiated by the archbishop, forbade the sale of indulgences in their dominions. While Tetzel could not enter Saxony, he set up a headquarters at Juterboch, only four miles from Wittenberg. Saxony was a prosperous area and Tetzel hoped thereby to attract *thalers* from Saxony into his coffers.

Multitudes flocked to him in order to secure the indulgences which promised relief from an indefinite period of suffering in eternity. Actually the indulgences were not distinguishable — and probably were not intended to be — from absolute pardon for sins which had been previously or would eventually be committed.

Martin Luther, planning to counteract the influence of Tetzel, began a series of sermons on salvation. He pointed out that salvation came by the grace of God. He had no intention of breaking with the Church but merely sought to show that the Church was subordinate to Christ, that Christ used the Church as the instrument for working out God's will upon the earth but that the Church could not promise that which Christ did not. The system of confession, penance, and absolution was merely an appendage to Christ's free grace. Salvation came through Christ, to be apprehended and appropriated by faith.

The test of Martin's preaching came when Martin received confessions. Several residents of Wittenberg informed him that they had been guilty of grave irregularities of conduct but added that they had purchased indulgences from Tetzel which had freed them from their guilt forever. In confirmation of their pardon they presented the letters of indulgence which they had received from Tetzel.

"This man cannot remit your sins," Martin advised them. "Only your own repentance and the grace of God can free you from your guilt."

"But he comes with absolute authority from the Holy Father," they protested. "Surely the Holy Father can remit your sins."

"These indulgences are mere scraps of paper," Martin informed them sternly. "They are altogether worthless."

"But we paid good money for them."

"It is money wasted," Martin replied. "They are not worth the paper on which they were written."

41

Many of the people who had made their confessions hastened back to Tetzel.

"Martin Luther says that these indulgences are worthless," they informed the Dominican. "Give us our money back."

Incensed, Tetzel condemned Martin's interference from the pulpit of the Juterboch church.

"This Augustinian monk speaks with no authority whatsoever," he said. "He is a heretic and should be burned at the stake. The Holy Father will know how to deal with him."

When Martin heard reports of Tetzel's sermon he wrote two letters. One was sent to the bishop of the diocese in which Tetzel was established and the other to the archiepiscopal prince of Mainz. He also condemned the action of Tetzel in a convocation which was held at the university, little dreaming as he did so that he was setting in motion a movement which would shake the foundations of the Church which he loved and in which he had served for many years.

In his epistles he assumed that the dignitaries to which he wrote were unaware of Tetzel's actions.

He therefore set down his charges on this wise:

> This traffic, which offends the laws of God and is contrary to all of the teachings of Christ, invites our people to sin. I implore you in the name of our Saviour and of His Church to put an end to it and banish from your jurisdiction this one who violates the laws of God. Surely you cannot be aware of what he is doing and the way in which he is harming the souls of these gullible people.

Evidently, however, they were well aware of the situation. They were also aware of the revenue which they were deriving from the traffic in indulgences, for one-half of Tetzel's receipts went into their treasuries while the other half was remitted to the pope. They, therefore, ignored Martin's protests and did not answer his letters.

Martin waited for a decent interval and, when he became convinced that no replies would be forthcoming, very reluctantly went into his pulpit and condemned the practice of selling indulgences. He spoke affectionately and yet forcefully, confident that he had back of him not only his own earnest conviction of the utter sinfulness of the practices in which Tetzel was engaged but that his position was sustained by the Church. Certainly, he believed, the pope would support him in the stand which he had taken. He was positive that the Holy Father would sustain him. The sermon which he preached hade a deep impression upon the crowd who listened to his words.

Having given public utterance to his convictions, Martin proceeded to set down in writing, according to the custom of his time, certain propositions. In some respects these propositions or theses, as they came to be called, were obscure and erroneous. He was still in the process of formulating his own thinking on the great doctrines of the Bible, still bound by the doctrines of the Church as they had been taught to him. Among the theses which he set forth were these cogent propositions:

1. When our Lord and Master, Jesus Christ, used the words, *"Penitentiam agite"* (do penance) He meant that the whole life of the faithful should be one of repentance.

5. The pope does not wish, nor is he able, to remit any penalty except what he or the Canon Law has imposed.

6. The pope cannot remit any condemnation; but can only declare, and confirm the remission that God Himself has given, except only in cases that belong to him. If he does otherwise the condemnation continues the same.

8. The laws of ecclesiastical penance can only be imposed on the living, and in no wise respect the dead.

22. The greater part of the people who have purchased indulgences will be deceived by this undistinguishing and pretentious promise which cannot be fulfilled.

25. The same power that the pope has over purgatory in the Church at large, is possessed by every bishop and every curate in his own particular diocese and parish.

28. It is certain that avarice is fostered by the money clinking in the chest, but to answer the prayers of the Church is in the power of God alone.

37. Every true Christian, alive or dead, participates in all of the goods of Christ and the Church without letters of pardon.

39. Yet we must not despise the pope's distributive and pardoning power; for his pardon is a declaration of God's pardon.

43. Christians are to be taught that if the pope knew the exactions of the preachers of indulgences, he would rather have St. Peter's church in ashes than have it built with the flesh and bones of his sheep.

62. The true treasure of the Church is the holy Gospel of the glory and grace of God.

94. We must exhort Christians to endeavor to follow Christ, their Head, under the cross, through death and hell.

95. For it is better through much tribulation to enter into the kingdom of heaven, than to gain a carnal eternity by the consolation of a false peace.

Such theses as the foregoing were decidely controversial but they did not deal with the heart of the problem which Martin was attacking. Included in the total were six theses which demonstrated exactly the practices of those who trafficked in papal indulgences. They read as follows:

27. Those persons preach human inventions who pretend that, at the very moment when the money sounds in the strong box, the soul escapes from purgatory. (This thesis had to do with the practice of selling indulgences on behalf of the dead.)

32. Those who fancy themselves sure of their salvation by indulgences, will go to the devil with those who teach them this doctrine.

42. We must teach Christians that the pope neither expects nor wishes us to compare the act of preaching indulgences with any charitable work whatsoever.

43. We must teach Christians that he who gives to the poor, or lends to the needy, does better than he who buys an indulgence.

45. We must teach Christians, that he who sees his neighbor in want, and, notwithstanding that, buys an indulgence, does not in reality acquire the pope's indulgence, and draws down on himself the anger of God.

53. They are the enemies of the pope and of Christ, who, to favor the preaching of indulgences, forbid the preaching of the Word of God.

From the foregoing it will be noted that in no place did Martin question the authority of the pope. He assumed, since he did not doubt his authority or challenge his sincerity as the vicar of Christ, that the pope would be on his side in the controversy with Tetzel. He believed, as a good Catholic, in the authority and supremacy of the pope and was confident that when the Holy Father was made aware of the abuses which were initiated by Tetzel he would immediately denounce the man.

Martin did not dream for a moment that the pope could possibly be a party to the whole scheme. Nevertheless, whether or not the pope would be on his side in the controversy, Martin felt compelled to take issue with a scheme which he regarded as altogether iniquitous and unchristian.

The die, therefore, was cast.

On the thirty-first of October, in 1517, he nailed the theses to the door of the parish church in Wittenberg. The theses were acknowledged by the signature written in a bold hand — "Martin Luther."

5

*I*F Luther had been content merely to post his theses on the church door and leave them there, it is quite possible that the entire matter would have blown over. The rain would have beaten against the pieces of paper, and the wind would have caught them up and carried them away. The whole affair would have been a topic of conversation in ecclesiastical and educational circles for a time and then would have been forgotten. But Luther persisted in keeping the matter alive. He arranged for the articles to be printed and they were immediately widely distributed.

If Martin had merely made his protest and let it rest, the people of Wittenberg would have talked about it for some time in the taverns and classrooms but consideration would have been local. However, Martin added to the flames which he had kindled, when he explained his theses at the morning service on November first in the castle church.

One of his brother monks caught the sleeve of his cloak at the close of the morning service and pulled him aside. He registered his protest mildly but earnestly, saying, "Dr. Martinus, you have gone too far. You will do our order considerable harm. The Dominicans, you know, are laughing up their sleeves at us."

His brother friar referred, of course, to the Augustinian Hermits when he used the pronoun "us." There was considerable rivalry between the Augustinians, to which both belonged, and the Dominicans.

Martin's good friend and adviser, Dr. Schurf, who was on the law faculty at the university, greeting him at the church door, shook his hand, but remarked sadly, "What is this that you are doing — writing and speaking against the pope? Do you realize what you have done? The pope's friends and advisers will not permit you to get away with it."

"But what if they have to permit it?" was Martin's only reply.

The pope, however, did not seem to be in the least disturbed. The monastic orders had been his staunch supporters, but they did create problems for him, for many of the monks took their vows much more seriously than did other ecclesiatics. When the pope heard what Martin had done he smilingly remarked, "Oh, it is of little importance. A drunken German has written some theses, but what matters that? When he sobers up he will speak differently."

It was the matter of printing the theses which made the difference. That and the fact that the Elector of Saxony, who was an earnest and pious prince, stood back of the young monk.

Nor did the pope realize just how much opposition had developed to the sale of the indulgences. If others had not been ready to condemn the practice publicly at least they did so in their own minds. There was widespread disaffection in the Church at this time. With the poverty that existed in most of the countries which made up the Holy Roman Empire and over which the Church had spiritual dominion there was, by contrast, an ostentatious display of wealth by most of the leading churchmen in Rome. Yet there were many other clerics who, although not vocal in their opposition, felt, like Luther, that the Church was not fulfilling the purpose for which Christ had established it.

They had in mind the fact that the Founder of the Church had been a poor carpenter who had described His own poverty when He said, "The Son of Man hath not where to lay His head." The Franciscan order of monks practiced the poverty which the Master had known. To be sure, all monks took perpetual vows of poverty but there were those, like Tetzel, upon whose consciences these vows were lightly held.

They remembered, too, that Peter, whom the Church maintained throughout the centuries was the first pope, had been a poor fisherman. How greatly had the Church departed from the condition in which it found itself at its beginning.

It should also be borne in mind that there was a considerable measure of nationalism among the countries included in Rome's dominion. The pope was traditionally an Italian and there were many, in Germany and France especially, who resented the domination of the Church by the Italian clergy.

Although their sympathies were with Martin, the rector of the

University of Wittenberg, and the prior of the Augustinian monastery to which Martin belonged, pleaded with him to drop the entire matter in order to avoid bringing the university and the Augustinian hermits into disfavor with the pope. Both of these fine men were advanced in years and had no desire to enter into controversies which might disturb the even temper of life in the institutions which they represented and over which they presided.

Martin's bishop bluntly ordered him to refrain from further utterance and distribution of copies of the theses. However, even if Martin had been inclined to obey the orders of his bishop and heed the injunctions of the rector and prior, he had set in motion a train of events which did not permit of cessation.

Martin had no conception of the enormity of the fire which he had kindled. His purpose in writing and publishing his theses had not been to occasion a break with the Church. He loved the Church and believed in its essential purposes. With the fire of youth, however, he merely sought to correct what he earnestly believed to be a long series of abuses within the Church. He had published his theses not because he was antagonistic to the Church but because he believed in it and loved it. He wanted to have the Church come to be regarded as an institution so free from taint that no one could level the finger of criticism against it.

When Luther's theses were being published, John Tetzel was in Frankfort where he was serving as inquisitor. His work had become exceedingly lucrative since he had singled out wealthy individuals whose lives had been unsavory and had persuaded them to purchase pardons for their sins. He was thoroughly incensed at the young monk and published an attack upon him.

Among the propositions which he set forth in answer to Martin's theses were the following:

3. Christians should be taught that the pope, in the plenitude of his power, is superior to the universal church, and superior to councils; and that entire subservience is due to his decrees.

4. Christians should be taught that the pope has the right to decide in questions of Christian doctrine; that he alone, and no other, has power to explain, according to his judgment, the sense of Holy Scripture, and to approve or condemn the words and works of others.

5. Christians should be taught that the judgment of the

pope, in things pertaining to Christian doctrine and those necessary to the salvation of mankind, can in no case err.

17. Christians should be taught that there are many things
which the church regards as certain articles of the Catholic faith,
although they are not found either in the inspired Scriptures or
in the early fathers.

The last-mentioned thesis provided Martin with further ammu-
nition for his crusade against the sale of indulgences. By this time
Martin had come to believe that the basic authority of the Church
did not rest with either popes or archbishops except as their pronouncements were in accord with the teachings of the Scriptures.
As between the authority of priests and that of the Bible, Martin
had to stand by the Bible.

However, Martin now went even further than that. In a
notable sermon, he challenged the pope's reasons for the sale of
indulgences and, by implication, criticized the lavish scale of living which he enjoyed.

"The pope does not need to sell indulgences in order to build
his cathedral," he asserted. "If he were so minded he could build
it with his own funds for he is richer than Croesus. Furthermore,
even if he did not have the means to complete the church it would
be much better to sell the unfinished building as it stands for the
relief of those who, in its erection, were defrauded in their purchase of ineffectual and worthless dispensations, or burn the whole
pile to the ground. To build it up with the blood and substance
of the poor is contrary to the will of God and the teachings of
Jesus Christ."

As might have been expected, among Luther's strongest adherents were his students. They were always greatly stimulated
by their teacher's forthright way of making his points in their classes.
He had a sense of humor, too, which communicated itself to the
students. Having experienced dire punishments in both his home
during his childhood and in school during his boyhood days, he
had no desire to punish his students for infractions of rules. He
felt that neither canings nor jibes constituted effective teaching. He
was also an enthusiastic pedagogue and the spontaneity of his educational process was readily communicated to his scholars.

When, therefore, the students discovered that copies of Tetzel's
attack upon Martin were being distributed in Wittenberg, they
organized groups to pick them up. They then arranged to build
a bonfire for the purpose of consigning to the flames all the copies

which they had picked up. It was an exceedingly hilarious occasion. Many older people came out to enjoy the fun of what was a typical student demonstration. But Martin was troubled by the event. He felt that this was no way to answer Tetzel's accusations. They should, instead, he declared, be answered from the pulpit or from a university lectern.

Concerning the bonfire he wrote later:

"I was not grieved that such a collection of extravagance and absurdity met with its just fate; but I did regret the manner in which the thing was done; and solemnly affirm that I knew nothing of it, neither did the elector or the magistrates."

Another strong ally proved to be the Elector, Frederick the Wise. Fearlessly he proclaimed himself on the side of Martin. Although he was no scholar and was probably unaware of the theological issues which were involved, he at least made it clear that he would protect Martin from any physical retaliation which might be planned for the young monk.

By this time the pope had begun to realize that "the drunken German," as he had called Martin, was attracting a considerable number of followers and took alarm. In February, 1518, he called upon the provincial-general of the Augustinian order and bade him take immediate action against the mistaken zealot in his company.

The provincial-general was an Italian, Gabriel della Volta. He passed on the order to Dr. Staupitz who was Martin's immediate superior and a man whom Martin loved and greatly admired. Staupitz tried to persuade Martin to recant.

"The Holy Father will recognize the fact that you are very young," he urged, "and that you are frequently moved to enthusiasm for a cause in which you firmly believe. I am confident that if you will recant, your punishment will not be too severe."

Then he added with a smile, "Believe what you will, Martin, but be not so outspoken in your expression of belief. When you attack Tetzel and the Dominicans so vociferously, you attack the pope, and when you attack him you attack the Church. There will always be some evils within the Church unfortunately, but we can correct them quietly from within."

"Would that I could accept your advice, dear friend," Martin said, "for you have been more than a father to me and my admiration and respect for you knows no bounds. But I cannot. Someone had to attack this wicked sale of indulgences. It was too flagrant to be attacked in the quiet of a monastery. It had to be brought out into the open."

"You are a stubborn man, Martin," Staupitz replied sadly, "but I love you for your stubbornness, much as I feel that you are choosing the wrong method of ridding the Church of this evil."

"My way is the only one I know," Martin replied quietly.

Staupitz reported to della Volta that he could not secure from Martin the statement which the general had demanded to the effect that he had been wrong. "Luther will not be satisfied until the sale of indulgences is stopped," Staupitz wrote, "and I assume that the Holy Father is not ready to command that such a step be taken."

The pope definitely was not. He ordered Martin to appear for trial in Rome on the charge, "Suspicion of heresy."

In the meantime, a conference of the Augustinians in the province of Saxony was convened at Heidelberg in April and May, 1518. Luther attended and immediately tendered his resignation from the office of district vicar of the order. He took this step in order to save his Augustinian brethren from further embarrassment on his behalf, but he steadfastly refused to withdraw any statement which he had made or to recant for the theses which he had written and published.

Instead, he delivered a retiring sermon, the basis of which was the set of principles upon which he had grounded his theses. His fellow monks listened to him attentively. This brother, who had been so obedient, so ready to do anything which a superior bade him undertake, had become a veritable whirlwind. This change in him astonished this group of humble and obedient men beyond measure.

When Martin returned from Heidelberg he began to work on the defense which he would put forward when he would go to Rome. The sixty-day period which the pope had determined should be the time allotted for him to reach Rome was already past. But the elector practically forbade him even to think of going to that capital city.

"You know what they would do to you there," he said bluntly.

"But the Holy Father has ordered me to go," Martin reminded the elector.

Exasperated, the latter inquired, "Look, now, Brother Martin, is it of any importance to the Church and to God that you live . . ."

Without waiting for the elector to complete his sentence Martin interposed, "Living or dying is of little importance."

". . . in order to correct those abuses against which you have been battling?" the elector concluded.

Martin was silent for a time, contemplating the elector's question. He knew beyond the peradventure of a doubt that he would not receive a fair trial in Rome. The court would have predetermined his guilt. If Martin should die, who would continue the battle against the iniquitous indulgence system? He was confident that John Staupitz felt as he did and he knew many other monks did also. But would any of them challenge this evil thing? He was well aware that the answer to his question was "no."

"I'll wait until they come for me," he promised the elector.

"And when they do they'll find my soldiers ready and waiting," the elector remarked grimly.

When Martin failed to put in his appearance in the Holy City, the pope became impatient, his impatience kindled especially by the needling of the Emperor Maximilian who had decided that for the financial welfare of his dominions, since he shared in the receipts from the sale of indulgences, Luther would have to be brought to trial.

Cardinal Cajetan, the pope's representative in Germany, suggested to the pope that Luther should be tried there. He felt that it would be a triumph for him if the monk would be dealt with in his diocese when Rome had failed to secure his presence there.

"He shall not escape lightly," he assured the pope, "but will be dealt with as he deserves."

The Elector Frederick still opposed the idea of Martin's leaving Saxony even though Martin would merely be going into another part of Germany.

"If you want to be tried let them try you here in our province," he argued. "You remember what happened to Huss when he went to Prague."

Martin remembered. Jan Huss had become his hero, and he could not forget that the one who had lighted the beacon which signalled the beginning of the Reformation had been burned at the stake. However, in Germany he would at least have an opportunity to be heard in his own defense.

"Let Christ live. Let Martin die," Luther said.

Finally the Elector agreed that Martin could go to Augsburg for the trial if the emperor would assure him safe-conduct. This the emperor agreed to do and Martin set out for Augsburg in the company of a group of friends, among them Dr. Staupitz.

When Martin and his companions reached Augsburg they discovered that the conference which had been called for the purpose of considering the charges against Martin had been adjourned. Only Cajetan remained to consider the incident. The cardinal was a capable diplomat and, at the outset of their meeting, his manner toward Martin seemed both conciliatory and reasonable.

But he was also very decided.

"You can understand, I am sure, Brother Martin, how much grief you have caused the Holy Father. He has many problems which he must face daily in combatting infidelity and sin. The weight of the evils of the world rests heavily upon his shoulders. When, therefore, one of his own priests criticizes him and the Church, it brings sorrow to his soul. Will you not, therefore, recant, ask to be forgiven, and become again a loyal priest?"

"If I can be shown wherein I am wrong, according to the teachings of God's Word, the Holy Bible, I will gladly recant," Luther told him earnestly. "I honor the pope as my spiritual leader, but for that very reason I would have him and the Church be so altogether above suspicion of having mercenary motives, that it would be impossible for them to have any traffic in the sale of indulgences."

The cardinal brought the tips of his long, tapered fingers together. He sensed that Luther was eager to make his peace with the pope, but that he could not do so unless his conscience approved.

"You said, did you not, that the treasury of the Church did not consist in the sufferings and merits of Christ?" he asked.

"I did," Luther agreed, "but I did not mean thereby that our Lord had not suffered greatly — more than anyone who ever lived — or that there was no merit in His life and death upon the cross. Instead, I pointed out that these could not be sold, that it was wrong to grant indulgences by attempting to impart Christ's merit and suffering to petitioners. We partake of His sufferings through faith: we obtain merit by becoming loyal followers of His."

The cardinal's eyes narrowed.

"And did you not also say that the sacrament of the Lord's Supper was of value only to those who had faith in the promise of God?" the cardinal continued. "Yet the Church has always taught that participation in the mass in and of itself, quite apart from the faith of the participant, gave merit. It is equally true of

53

prayers, we know. The repetition of 'Hail, Marys' and the 'Our Father,' together with other prescribed petitions, in and of themselves grant merit to the participants."

"I also said that," Martin acknowledged. "Of what value is a sacrament unless the participant comes to accept it in a spirit of devotion and then through faith receives it?"

Cajetan's eyes blazed with anger. This monk was evidently in no mood to recant. The dissenting cleric had come to Cajetan to debate, evidently — not to plead for forgiveness. Furiously the cardinal shouted, "Go away. Recant or do not come again before my eyes."

Martin bowed to his superior and then, with head held high, left the presence of the Church's emissary. He had what he considered judgment pronounced against him. There would be no point, therefore, in planning to return for further conferences.

Later the cardinal remarked to Dr. Staupitz, "I will no longer dispute with that beast, for it has deep eyes and fearful speculations in its head."

Cardinal Cajetan made his way back to Rome, Martin to Wittenberg.

"He was recalcitrant, unrepentant, argumentative," Cajetan reported to the pope. "You would be justified if you excommunicated him."

The pope pondered the suggestion. That Martin Luther was a heretic he had no doubt: whenever an individual questioned the decisions or actions of the pope or a council, such an action was indubitably heresy and he would be justified in formally declaring Luther to be a heretic. But the pope was also politic. By this time Martin's following had grown exceedingly. If he were excommunicated there would be many who would flock to his banner. If Martin was not aware of this, the pope was. He knew that there was much discontent in the Church. Cajetan dealt only with German princes and clergymen, but the pope dealt with situations in England, Scotland, Spain, France, and in the seat of his government, Italy, as well. He would soon be dealing with colonies to be established in the New World. It was easy enough for Cajetan to dismiss the matter, but this Luther was not one to be dealt with hastily: he was evidently a determined — if mistaken — man, the pope decided, and then admitted ruefully to himself, a man who was well versed in the Scriptures.

The pope bethought himself of Charles von Miltitz who was, in a sense, a minister without portfolio in the papal court. Von Miltitz was a Saxon count with the official rank of apostolic chamberlain. He was exceedingly astute and he knew the temper of the German people, especially the Saxons. Yet he had lived in Rome for so long and had been so active in the diplomatic activities of the papacy that he was thoroughly cognizant of the issues involved in a conflict between the papacy and either the members of the German clergy or noblemen.

The pope was confident that the appointment of Von Miltitz would not only please and appease the elector, but would do much to pacify the recalcitrant Martin.

Before conferring with Martin, von Miltitz sounded out the various elements in Saxony. He discovered that three out of every four people took the side of Martin Luther. It was one thing to discipline a monk who espoused an unpopular cause: it was something else again, as he knew, to discipline one who championed a movement which the majority of people approved.

Von Miltitz, therefore, approached a conference with Luther diplomatically. He told Martin that he agreed with him that Tetzel was a fraud. Like Luther, he condemned the indulgences, but with a smile he remarked, "There are different ways of dealing with such a situation. Your way is that of the sword. You would fight against it with bludgeon strokes. I prefer to use the ways of diplomacy. We are both agreed that indulgences should be done away. Since we love the Church and do not want to see it suffer will you not agree to try my way now?"

Luther pondered the question.

"What would be your way?" he inquired finally.

"I would suggest that we call a halt to the debate until you are given a fair trial before an enlightened bishop, one who would be friendly to you and sympathetic to your point of view as well as fair to the Church," von Miltitz replied.

That had been all that Martin wanted. He had had no desire to divide the Church. It had merely been his earnest hope that the Church should be purged of all practices which were contrary to the will of God. The proposition seemed to be altogether fair and Martin agreed to it.

After the conference was concluded, Martin wrote the following report to the elector:

Let me humbly inform your Grace that Charles von Miltitz and I have at last come to an agreement and concluded our negotiations by the adoption of two articles:

Both sides shall be inhibited from preaching, writing and acting further in the matter.

Miltitz will write to the Pope at once, informing him how things stand, and asking him to commit the matter to some learned bishop, who will hear me and point out the errors I am to recant: for, when I have learned what my errors have been, I will gladly withdraw them, and do nothing to impair the honor and power of the Roman Church.

It seemed as if the matter had been settled. Luther would be brought to trial but it would be a hearing in which he would be treated fairly. Of that Martin was confident. For the time being he had promised not to engage in a disputation with the heirarchy. On the other hand, he would be free from criticism by other members of the clergy. Eventually, beyond doubt, the matter would be settled to the satisfaction of the pope and his own conscience.

Von Miltitz was altogether satisfied with the results of the conference also and communicated the news of the happy termination of the controversy to the pope.

6

*I*N the summer of 1518 a new professor had been added to the faculty of the University of Wittenberg, Philip Melancthon, a grand-nephew of the humanist, Johann Reuchlin. At sixteen, Philip had taken his bachelor of arts degree, at seventeen his degree of master of arts. Born in 1497 in the town of Bretton in the Palatinate, he was just under twenty-one years of age when he was appointed to the chair of Greek in the Elector Frederick's new university. Philip, for all his scholastic achievements, appeared more youthful still than his twenty-one years when he stood beside Martin Luther.

Cajetan had written to the Elector Frederick demanding that Martin should be sent as a prisoner to Rome since the cardinal claimed that he had won over him in their debate and that Luther had refused to renounce the heretical position which he held. Frederick refused to accede to the demand. Several factors probably influenced the decision. First of all, the elector was exceedingly proud of the university and Martin Luther was the one professor who had brought fame to the school. To some, because of Martin's association with the university, the name of the school was anathema. They characterized the institution as a hotbed of atheism and heresy. To others it was a symbol of hope, a symbol of rebellion against Rome. Doubtless the second reason for his refusal was his sterling character. He was an exceedingly independent person and, although his kingdom was small, it was strong.

Frederick thought to add luster to the university by appointing Melancthon to the important post of professor of Greek. Philip Melancthon's given name was Philip Schwarzerd but he had changed his name to its Greek equivalent, a common practice in those days.

If Martin Luther was a firebrand, Philip was a cool stream of water. Perhaps because of the difference in their temperaments they became fast friends. Luther became Philip's hero: Philip, who was only fourteen years younger than Martin became as a son to him. The friendship between the two developed at once and shortly after Philip's arrival Martin wrote to Spalatin who had been instrumental in securing Philip for his professorship at the university, paying tribute to the latter:

> Doubt not that we have done all and shall do all you recommend about Philip Melancthon. He delivered an oration the fourth day after he came, in the purest, and most learned style, by which he won the thanks and admiration of all, so that you need not worry about commending him to us. We quickly abandoned the opinion which we had formed because of his small stature and homely appearance, and now rejoice and wonder at his real worth, and thank our most illustrious Elector and your good offices, too, for obtaining his services for us. While Philip is alive I desire no other Greek teacher.

As professor of the Bible, of course, Philip's excellent instruction in Greek aided Martin's students in preparation for the courses which they took under him. Philip gave the students the background which they needed for their studies with Martin.

On another occasion, Martin described the difference between Philip and himself in these words:

> I am rough, boisterous, stormy and altogether warlike. I am born to fight against innumerable monsters and devils. I must remove stumps and stones, cut away thistles and thorns, and clear wild forests; but Master Philip comes along softly and gently, sowing and watering with joy, according to the gifts which God has abundantly bestowed upon him.

For some considerable time there was a quiet period in the controversy of which Martin had been the center. He had no desire to revive the dispute even though he described himself as boisterous and warlike. Tetzel, who had been the cause of the storm in the beginning, was working elsewhere. However, at the University of Ingolstadt, there was a professor on the faculty, Johann Maier Eck. He published a series of theses on the debate, although they did not mention Martin by name. During the first week of the debates between Carlstadt and Eck the matter under discussion was free will. Eck was definitely the winner. The next week, with Luther taking Carlstadt's place, they debated the subject of the primacy of the pope and the authority of church councils. During the third week the subject of the debate was the orthodox view of the church regarding indulgences, penance, purgatory, and the powers which priests possessed to grant absolution to sinners.

Luther discovered, as he developed his arguments, that he was destroying many of the beliefs which he had formerly held. It was as if he was digging his way out of a dungeon, out of an imprisonment whereby his mind had been in bondage for a lifetime. One step led to another. In many respects the pattern of the Reformation which he began was forged at Leipzig. He had probably not realized until he confronted Eck just how far his own thinking had strayed from the conservative doctrines of the Church.

The debates also put his warmest friends into an embarrassing situation. Hitherto they had excused Martin for his impetuous decisions. They regarded him as a young man, groping for the truth. This was the way of youth. Now, when he was openly declaring himself in a manner so altogether contradictory to the beliefs which the Church held, they had to declare themselves. Sadly and reluctantly Staupitz, Martin's warm friend for several decades, arrayed himself against Martin, to Luther's great sorrow. Others, who had warmly supported him, also fell away, but to Philip Melancthon, Martin was more of a hero than ever before.

Other equally far-reaching events were occurring, especially in the field of politics. With the death of Maximilian, it was necessary to elect his successor as emperor of the Holy Roman empire. The new emperor was Charles of Spain, the grandson of Maximilian. If Maximilian had been lukewarm to the papacy, Charles, at least at the beginning of his reign, was its loyal defendant.

The new emperor was altogether unconcerned about the views of the elector of Saxony, and Charles joined the pope in ordering Frederick to turn Luther over to Rome for trial. Again the elector came to Martin's defense, defying the pope and thereby putting himself in jeopardy. He refused to give Luther up.

The pope and his advisers prepared a bull which, although it did not cite Luther by name, was prepared especially against him. It was signed June 28, 1519, and was entitled, "*Exsurge Domine*," taking its title from the first words of the document which read, "Arise, Lord, plead Thine own cause. Arise and protect the vineyard which thou gavest Peter, from the wild beast who is devouring it." The "beast" was given sixty days in which to recant his errors. In the event that he should obdurately refuse to do so, he would be branded "a stiff-necked, notorious, damned heretic," and excommunication would follow.

The lines were now definitely drawn. Martin either had to recant or be forever branded as a hated heretic, and the elector was ordered to yield Martin up to papal authorities or suffer reprisals. It was sometime during this period that Martin had a colloquy with someone whom he identified as the devil. The conversation between the reformer and Satan has been explained in many ways. As far as Martin was concerned, the devil was a very real personage who appeared to him in corporeal form.

By way of explaining Martin's point of view, it should be said that when he interpreted the story of Christ's temptations in the wilderness, he accepted the view that Satan also appeared to Jesus in human form. Martin did not accept the explanation that this was a spiritual battle which the Son of God waged with the evil one. It was an actual confrontation of two personages who met face to face on the Mount of Temptation.

Consequently for Martin, too, the devil was altogether real, a malign personality who could be seen, who could speak and hear spoken words. Beelzebub was not a figment of an overwrought imagination. He was a person, malevolent, suave, insinuating. As Martin worked at his desk, preparing an answer to the pope's bull, he considered all of the factors which would be involved if he yielded.

According to Martin, Satan advised repentance for having defied the pope, literally advocating that Martin plead "guilty" to all of the errors with which he had been charged. If he would advance such a plea, he would doubtless be forgiven and received by the pontiff as an erring but penitent son. To be sure, he would have to make penance of some kind but the pope would undoubtedly assign to him some task which would not be too difficult of accomplishment.

Satan also warned Martin of the consequences of continued obduracy. Was he willing to be responsible for the development of another schism in the Church? As a keen student of church history, Martin was aware that the Church which he loved had been divided sharply into two branches: the western, which was known as the "Catholic" Church, the one to which he had pledged his allegiance when he became a monk, and the eastern, known as the "Orthodox" Church. This had happened centuries before, but the two parts had never been reunited. Was Martin now willing to encourage this same thing to come to pass?

Because of his love for the Church and his devotion to it, for by now he was probably aware of what the consequences of his own stand would be, Martin was tempted to recant. After all, what did the feelings of one obscure German monk matter in the development of the Church? It would not only be the easiest way out of the dilemma, it would also be the way which would preserve the Church intact.

Martin could not envisage all of the results of the Reformation, to be sure, but he knew, from the size of the following which had already gathered around him, that division might be in prospect.

Yet the inner voice whispered to him, "But what about truth, Martin? Can a church which would be built upon half-lies be truly the Church of the Lord Jesus Christ? Can a church which trades upon human credulity, the eagerness to escape long periods of time in purgatory — for the existence of which there was not even any justification in Scripture — be the Church whose formation and development had been foretold by the Lord Jesus Christ when He said that 'the gates of hell would not prevail against it' or be the Church of its Founder, Jesus Christ, the Saviour of mankind?"

Martin could envision the devil leering over his shoulder.

"Recant, Martin, recant," Satan urged. "Recant in the name of unity. Recant and preserve the Church. The Church will always have its Tetzels. That is inevitable. The Church can never be altogether perfect. That is too much to expect of it. It numbers within its membership imperfect priests and imperfect members, but Paul has reminded us that there is none perfect save Christ Himself. Recant, therefore, and become again a loyal priest and a true son of the Church."

Martin picked up an inkwell and threw it at the personage whom he confidently believed was there in the room with him. The inkwell hit the wall of his study, splattering ink over it. The ink ran down to the floor and spread in an ever-widening pool.

"Never!" Martin said aloud. "God helping me, here I stand!"

It was about this time also that Martin turned to his former love, music, and composed a song which was to become the battle hymn of the Reformation, "A Mighty Fortress Is Our God." As the words came from his pen, his spirits soared with both the lyrics and the music. It was a crude effort of composition at first, and Martin did not give it to his friends until 1529, but he often played

61

the music, occasionally changing notes and words, until he felt that he had both a text and music which satisfied his own critical senses.

This hymn, which has come down to the present, is a stirring call to action. The music is perfectly wedded to the sturdy words with which, in rousing tones, the hymn begins. The text actually loses much by translation from the gutteral German tongue in which they were written but there are no English equivalents for the strong words of the original tongue. The final result of his attempts to find a hymn which would perfectly convey the spirit of the Reformation was:

A mighty Fortress is our God,
A bulwark never failing;
Our Helper He, amid the flood
Of mortal ills prevailing.
For still our ancient foe
Doth seek to work us woe;
His craft and pow'r are great;
And, armed with cruel hate,
On earth is not his equal.

Did we in our own strength confide,
Our striving would be losing;
Were not the right Man on our side,
The Man of God's own choosing.
Dost ask who that may be?
Christ Jesus, it is He;
Lord Sabaoth His name,
From age to age the same,
And He must win the battle.

And though this world, with devils filled
Should threaten to undo us,
We will not fear, for God hath willed
His truth to triumph through us.
The prince of darkness grim —
We tremble not for him;
His rage we can endure,
For lo! his doom is sure,
One little word shall fell him.

That word above all earthly powers —
No thanks to them, abideth;
The Spirit and the gifts are ours
Through Him who with us sideth.

Let goods and kindred go,
This mortal life also;
The body they may kill;
God's truth abideth still,
His Kingdom is forever.

The sixty days following publication of the papal bull had passed without Martin recanting, but the pope failed to take action immediately thereafter as he had threatened to do. He was actually in no hurry to do so or quite possibly the affair had slipped his mind or he may have felt that the threat of excommunication was actually all that was needed to put the German monk in his place. But the matter had not slipped Martin's mind. The middle of October, Luther wrote a letter to the pope in which he said:

> Father Leo, beware how you listen to those sirens who make you no more man, but a demigod, so that you can command and exact whatever you will. It will not be so always nor will you prevail, for you are a servant of servants . . . Let them not deceive you who pretend that you are Lord of the world.

A few weeks later, Martin, still confident that his superior, Spalatin, would see that the action which he had taken was not that of a renegade but was, instead, the deed of a loyal churchman, wrote to his superior, condemning the bull once more and saying:

> Never since the beginning of the world has Satan spoken so shamelessly against God as he hath expressed himself in this bull. It is impossible for anyone who accepts it, and does not contest it, to be saved.

This was exceedingly strong language for a cleric to utter, thereby indicating that the pope had been influenced by Satan himself, but Martin felt that the Church could not possibly approve of the actions of the pope, and that, in selling indulgences, the pope had engaged in a program which the Church could not accept as Christian. He was also confident that he had back of him the approval of the vast majority of the clergy. True, he would have acted as he did with or without the approbation of his fellows, but he sincerely believed that the heart of the Church was right and that the men who had entered the priestly orders would sustain him.

For this reason he appealed from the pope to a general council, confident that such a council would not only vindicate him but would probably also set limits to the authority which the Roman pontiff could exercise.

With this in mind, he published a very violent pamphlet in which he denounced the bull. Needless to say, because of the publicity which had been given to the proclamation of the bull and his defiance of it, he became one of the best-known men in Germany. From relative obscurity he was catapulted into a place in the limelight. Almost overnight an unknown monk began to be both praised and condemned by people in even the most remote regions of Germany and in other countries as well.

His books, too, had begun to have a wide circulation. They were read not only in Germany but in Switzerland, France and England. They were purchased eagerly by university people and clerics as well. Many of those who bought the books sought to find flaws in their reasoning in order to condemn them. Others, eager for a champion to espouse their own opposition to sale of indulgences, were cheered and heartened by them.

In Louvain and Cologne, the bishops ordered the collection and burning of all Martin's writings, and at both places bonfires were kindled and the heretical volumes consigned to the flames. One result of this activity, to be sure, was to call attention in all of the countries of Europe to Martin. Some priests preached sermons in which they insisted that Martin was anti-Christ. Very few, except in Germany, dared to praise Luther, but he started men thinking and people eagerly awaited news of what he was doing and saying.

When Martin heard about the book-burning episode he decided to answer in kind. In December, 1520, Martin posted a sign on the bulletin board of the university inviting students and members of the faculty to meet in front of the Church of the Holy Cross which was located outside the Elster Gate of the city of Wittenberg.

Some of the professors, disdaining the notice, tried to hold classes, but the classrooms were empty. The rest of the professors and probably the majority of the students met at the appointed place. Just before nine o'clock, Martin Luther, the monk who was also their most admired professor, appeared and kindled a fire of faggots which he had gathered alongside the road.

When he had a good fire going he announced in a clear and resonant voice: "I have in my hand the bull which was prepared by Pope Leo X — may God preserve him — in which it is noted that I have been excommunicated. I earnestly denounce this document and declare that it is impossible for his holiness to excommunicate me. If I have done wrong, then may God, in His infinite wisdom, deny me the sacrament of holy communion. If I have done right, may the Creator and Preserver of us all vindicate me. I also declare that I am appealing to a council of the Church, asking that its members judge me, for only a council may decide whether what I have done was right or wrong."

Then, consigning the bull to the flames, he said, "Because thou didst trouble the holy one of the Lord, may eternal fire consume thee!"

Cheers rebounded from the city walls as the students rent the air with their cheers. School was over as far as their attendance upon classes for that day was concerned. The students did not wait for any announcement by the regent of the university. They began to parade the streets, singing the *Te Deum* as they marched. As they went past homes and places of business, they solicited papal books which they might add to the flames. Enough were thus obtained to keep the fire going the entire day.

7

*A*GAIN there came a demand by leading clerics that Martin should be sent to Rome to be tried officially.

Martin remarked drily to Philip, "But I have already been tried. The pope himself has passed sentence upon me. My penalty, according to the pope's decree, has been excommunication. I would assume that, having been once excommunicated, I can scarcely be excommunicated again."

To be sure, Martin had neither accepted nor observed the penalty. While his teaching responsibilities occupied so much of his time at Wittenberg that he rarely conducted mass or heard confessions, still there was no attempt to interfere with him in any way: thus the bull changed in no way the tenor of his life.

Martin was offered a safe-conduct to Rome, but by this time he had decided that it would be foolish to trust such a safe-conduct. If he were to be tried it would have to be in Germany.

Having achieved a perfect understanding with the new emperor, Charles V, Pope Leo turned the matter of a trial over to him. The emperor planned to conduct, in Worms, his first diet since assuming the crown. A diet was a name customarily given to an assembly called by the emperor, upon his own initiative, to discuss political and ecclesiastical matters with conferees of his own choice. The word "diet" came from the Latin word, *"dies,"* —a day. The word came to mean, in political parlance, a day set apart for some special purpose, assemblage or discussion.

Ostensibly the Diet of Worms was convened by the emperor for the purpose of acquainting himself with the politics of the German states. Since he was a Spaniard, and France was independent of the empire, Germany was separated from the other portions of his realm by a wide boundary which was actually a buffer country. Charles informed the pope that his purpose would be to sound out the feeling of princes and ecclesiastics in other areas of Germany before he would actually bring Luther to trial.

Thus, while the diet began its sessions in January, it was March before the summons came to Luther to attend the meeting. In the meantime his friends were doing all in their power to aid him.

His superior, Spalatin, urged him to make his peace with the pope before attending the diet and warned him of the dangers inherent in a trial. Spalatin did not approve Luther's stand, but he was exceedingly fond of his tempestuous monk and concerned for his safety. He was also concerned for the good name of the Augustinian Hermits and the welfare of the Church. He felt that the death of one more so-called "heretic" would be another black mark on the Church's record.

"Don't go to Worms," he cautioned. "The emperor will undoubtedly condemn you to death or your enemies might even kill you before you arrive at the meeting-place."

However Martin was determined. "I will go if I am carried sick in my bed. I am called of the Lord when the emperor summons me. Further, if they intend violence, as is very likely, my case is to be commended to the Lord. The same Lord lives and reigns who preserved the three youths in the fiery furnace of Babylon, and if He does not choose to preserve me, my head is a very small thing in comparison with Christ, who was slain with the utmost ignominy. I trust that the emperor will not begin his reign by shedding innocent blood. I would rather be murdered by them of Rome."

The elector also summoned Martin for a conference.

"You are in as much danger in Worms as you would be if you went to Rome," he warned, "and I cannot protect you in Worms as I could in Saxony. Don't go, I beg of you. Alive, you can lead the forces of reform. Dead, of what value are you to the cause?"

"I must go," Martin announced decisively. "Our Lord and Master was warned before He went to Jerusalem that dangers awaited Him there. How can I do less than He?"

The elector shrugged his shoulders. What could he do with such a stubborn character?

"At least I can arrange to give you an escort," he said, "if you have completely made up your mind to go."

"I have," Luther replied.

Within a few days Martin received the official summons to the trial which read:

Charles, by the grace of God Emperor elect of the Romans,

Honorable, well-beloved and pious — We and the states of the holy empire here assembled, having resolved to institute an inquiry touching the doctrine which you have openly espoused and the books which you have lately published, for your coming hither, and your return to a place of security, our safe-conduct and that of the empire, which we send you herewith. Our sincere desire is, that you should prepare immediately for this journey, in order that within the space of twenty-one days fixed by our safe-conduct, you may without fail be present before us. Fear neither injustice nor violence. We will firmly abide by our aforesaid safe-conduct, and expect that you will comply with our summons. In so doing you will obey our earnest wishes . . .

Given in our imperial city of Worms, the sixth day of March, in the year of our Lord, 1521, and the second of our reign.

CHARLES

Martin set out with the emperor's herald a few days later. The messenger was on horseback, and Martin rode in an open wagon, a vehicle which was roofed and also protected from rain or snow by leather curtains around the sides which could be drawn tight during inclement weather. Before leaving Wittenberg Martin addressed the crowd of people who had gathered to wish him Godspeed.

"Pray not for me," he said, "but for the word of God. The papists do not desire my coming to Worms, but my condemnation and my death. It matters not. Before my blood has grown cold, thousands of men in the whole world will have become responsible for having shed it. The most holy adversary of Christ, the father, the master, the generalissimo of murderers, insists on its being shed. So be it. Let God's will be done. Christ will give me His Spirit to overcome these ministers of error. I despise them during my life; I shall triumph over them by my death. They are busy at Worms about compelling me to retract; and this shall be my retraction; I said formerly that the pope was Christ's vicar: now I assert that he is our Lord's adversary and the devil's apostle."

Heretofore Martin had apparently believed that the pope had been misled by his advisers: now he had become convinced that the pope himself was a menace to Christendom. Quite evidently he also believed that, despite the emperor's safe-conduct, he was destined for either assassination or death by condemnation. He greatly feared what would probably happen at Worms and yet felt compelled to go there.

It was nearly three hundred miles from Wittenberg to Worms, and Martin passed through many towns and villages en route. He was alternately cheered and jeered as he drove through the towns. At Naumberg, a priest, who was a friend of his, invited Martin into his study. When Luther was seated, the priest took down from the wall a picture of Savanorola which had been hanging there. Without saying a word, he held up the portrait as a silent warning of what might happen to Martin in Worms. Undaunted, Luther continued the journey.

At Erfurt, Martin was escorted through town by a party of horsemen, stopping en route at the Augustinian church which was packed with people who had evidently come there expecting to hear him. Martin was in a hurry to press on, but he could not disappoint the Erfurt people, many of whom were his warm friends. Again Martin issued the challenge to the clergy to cleanse the Church, citing the story of Jesus' cleansing of the temple.

"Differing from the time of our Lord," he said, "it is now not a single church in which trafficking is practiced as it was in Jesus' day. It is not just one temple as it was then. Wherever the emissaries of the pope have gone they have turned churches into houses of commerce although our Master said, 'Make not my Father's house an house of merchandise. My Father intended it for worship but ye have made it a den of thieves.'"

It heartened Martin greatly to see some of his fellow Augustinians nodding their heads in approval. Apparently he was obtaining the support of many in the clergy as well as the laity and the nobility.

At Erfurt he also had another bout with the illness which had plagued him for years and which was to continue to remain with him throughout his life, but he made nothing of it and pressed on, escorted by the horsemen until he was well out in the countryside when his fellow monks bade him a warm farewell. When he arrived in Oppenheim other friends greeted him and warned him of the possible fate which might await him as, a century before, it had befallen Jan Huss.

Impatiently Martin replied to his friends' warnings, "Huss was burned, to be sure, but the truth was not consumed along with his body. If there be as many devils in Worms as tiles on the roof-tops, I will enter."

It seemed that every warning which he received merely caused his courage and confidence to increase. Or possibly the reason for the development of these two virtues lay in the discovery that so many German people were on his side. He had heard reports in Wittenberg of the popular response which was meeting news of his defiance of papal authority, but he did not know just how much credence he could give to such reports. Now he was actually experiencing the response about which he had heard.

Worms, although almost wholly destroyed during the Thirty Years War which was to occur some years later, was at this time one of the important cities of the empire. The minster was built of red sandstone and was an exceedingly imposing edifice. As Luther approached the city in his wagon a trumpeter blew his horn from the vantage point of the Tower Gate to announce his arrival. People immediately thronged the streets to catch a glimpse of the monk who had defied the pope. Townspeople mingled with the many distinguished visitors, princes and nobles, prelates and abbots, who had been summoned by the emperor.

When he was made aware of Luther's arrival, the papal nuncio suggested to the emperor that Luther should be lodged in a cell in the dungeon of the castle, but the emperor refused to treat Martin in this manner.

"As far as our empire is concerned, the man is not a prisoner even though the Holy Father has excommunicated him. You have had reports of his triumphal progress across Germany on his way hither. To imprison him immediately after his arrival would stir up these people against us. We must give every indication of our intention to be completely unbiased in our dealings with the monk," the emperor announced.

He added, "As evidence of the esteem in which he is held I should tell you that the Knights of St. John have indicated that they would like to have him as a guest in their quarters."

Charles V was only twenty-one years of age at this time, and he was attending his first diet. He was eager to win the approval of the people of his realm, particularly of the Germans in whose country the diet had been convened. He was also anxious to remain in the good graces of the pope and his prelates but at the moment concern for the good will of the Germans outweighed the other consideration.

The time for Luther's trial was set for four o'clock on the afternoon of April 17, 1521. The young emperor had set the stage for the occasion most carefully. He sat on a throne raised well above the seats of the members of his court. Included in the group arrayed around and somewhat below him were his brother, Ferdinand; the papal nuncios, Aleander and Caracciolo; the electors, including Frederick of Saxony; and also representatives of the free cities of Germany.

Martin, outside the great hall of the minister, waited to be summoned. Just before the hour appointed for the beginning of his trial, a marshal and herald came out of the great hall and into the anteroom to summon him. In the streets around the minister were crowds of people, jostling and pushing, pressing in so close that there was no room for late-comers among the counsellors to push their way through the horde.

If the young emperor thought to intimidate the simple monk by the magnificence of the forces arrayed against him he failed to accomplish his end. Martin was impressed, to be sure; his heart beat faster than usual. Yet Luther saw the group gathered about the emperor as people to be won over to the cause of reformation, a challenging opportunity to explain the position which he had taken. The reformation which he had in mind, to be sure, was not the formation of a new church but the purification of the only Church which he knew.

Although his face was pale, his step did not falter as he entered the hall and confronted the emperor. His gaze, as it swept over the company of advisers and courtiers, was direct and searching.

The emperor turned to one who stood at his elbow. "This man," he whispered, "will never make a heretic of me."

Charles turned to the prosecutor, at that time called, "trier," and remarked briefly, "Read the charges."

The trier unfolded the document and, in a loud voice, intoned: "Martin, the Emperor has summoned you hither for two ends. First, to say whether or not you have published these books." At this point he indicated a pile of books and pamphlets on the table. "Secondly," he continued, "he would have you inform his majesty whether you intend to recant or to abide by the teachings contained therein."

He gestured to one of his assistants and said, "Let the titles of the books be read out." As if afraid of being contaminated, a clerk picked up the offending books one by one and read the titles of each. Martin listened intently to the reading of their names.

"These are your books, are they not?" the emperor inquired.

Very gravely Martin acknowledged authorship, saying, "The books are mine. I do not deny writing them. But I would, if it pleases your majesty, ask for time to prepare my defense if I am to be tried on the basis of their contents. The charge, indeed, is a serious one, involving the question of faith and the salvation of souls, and I should be given time so that I may answer without injury to the divine. Word or peril to my soul."

Frederick nodded his head in approbation.

The emperor, without glancing at his ecclesiastical counsellors, replied, "This would seem to be a reasonable request. We will grant you a day's time."

Martin returned to his lodgings where he spent the night in prayer. There were many in Worms who were his friends and sympathizers. He remembered that, when he had entered the great hall that afternoon, a grizzled captain in the imperial guard had laid a hand on his shoulder and said, "Monk, beware what you do; you are in more danger than any of us have ever faced on the field of battle: but if you are on the right road, go forward in God's name, and be sure that He will not forsake you!"

"O Lord," Martin prayed, "I cannot desert men like him. They are depending upon me to announce and defend the truth. Grant me courage sufficient to do so."

There were times during the night, however, as he contemplated the host of enemies who had gathered in the hall the previous afternoon when it seemed to him that he had been forsaken by God.

At one such moment when he felt especially isolated he prayed, "Dost Thou want me to proclaim the truth?"

Even as he questioned, it seemed to him that the answer came. God could want nothing else. God would not have His Church built upon falsehood, deceit. Yet there were moments, again, when it seemed to him that God had forsaken him. When those doubts arose, he recalled the fact that Jesus Himself on Calvary had prayed, "My God, my God, why hast Thou forsaken me?"

If the Master had sensed the loneliness of that dread hour, why should Martin be spared the experience? He finally found surcease in a few hours of troubled sleep.

Martin appeared at the great hall promptly at four o'clock on the afternoon of April 18th, but he was kept waiting outside

72

the hall for two hours while the counsellors attended to other matters. There was no question but that the major issue which the members of the diet had to consider was that of the actions of the monk from Wittenberg, but the imperial orator, Eyk, assumed that if Martin could be kept waiting for a long enough period, he would be less confident when he appeared once more before the tribunal.

When he was admitted, Martin was questioned immediately by Eyk.

"You have had twenty-four hours in which to write your retraction," Eyk bluntly told him, fixing Martin with a piercing gaze. "Is your statement ready?"

"I have spent the major part of that time in prayer," Martin replied. "There is no retraction nor do I intend to write any unless I can be convinced that the statements which I made were untrue."

"Then, your majesty, I would point out to your grace that the heretical volumes which you see before you alone condemn this man," Eyk announced, pointing dramatically to Martin's books and pamphlets. "You can see what a mountain of untruth we have here."

Johann Schurff, one of Martin's associates at Wittenberg, jumped to his feet. He was there solely in the role of a spectator but he could not keep silence.

"May it please your majesty," Schurff asked, "to inquire if the *trier* has read these volumes?"

Charles V looked at Eyk who colored under his scrutiny.

"Your majesty," Eyk said, "I must acknowledge that I have not read all of these scurrilous books and pamphlets. I would hesitate to do so in light of the fact that to read them would be to subject myself to heretical ideas and teachings."

"Then, your majesty, how is it possible to indict my colleague on the basis of books which he has written, but which the *trier* has not even read and with whose contents he is naturally wholly unfamiliar?" Schurff retorted.

Eyk's eyes narrowed. His face turned crimson.

"I have read enough to know that they are all heretical," he stiffly asserted.

"That is most interesting," Schurff remarked softly. "I have read many of these works myself — not all, I will admit — but I found that those which I read were profound expository works, based on the teachings of the Holy Scriptures. Surely the *trier* cannot object if such a notable scholar as Dr. Luther, who has been appointed a professor of the Bible and a teacher of theology in the University of Wittenberg, should set down his teachings in book and pamphlet form. Or does he insist that the mere writing of a book is heretical?"

Smiling, Martin Luther stood in his place.

"Perhaps, your majesty," he said, "I may be permitted to speak of these works myself. You will note, Sire, that I have written a considerable number of books. I think that I may safely say that the vast majority of these works would be approved by the *trier* if he had read them. Many of them are expositions of various parts of Holy Scripture and I believe that most scholars would agree, as does Dr. Schurff, with my findings in these fields of study.

"In fact, your majesty, I would go so far as to say that failure to accept my delineation of these portions of Scriptures would be, in effect, to deny the authenticity of the Bible. These works were written for the purpose of encouraging Christians to develop in their characters a sturdy faith and Christian moral standard. Even my accusers, I am confident, would admit that these were written in a thoroughly Scriptural and profitable manner. For me to retract these writings would be to deny certain principles upon which all parties to this controversy agree. They are, in fact, essential to good order and the welfare of human society.

"A few of the other works, I grant you, constitute an attack upon the abuses of the papacy, and particularly the sale of indulgences, a practice which has neither the authority of the Holy Scriptures to authenticate it, nor the custom of the Church for all past centuries, but is wholly a modern innovation designed to obtain funds for the erection of St. Peter's Church in Rome. These spurious doctrines, by which certain priests have impoverished our people, fettered their reasons, and assisted in destroying their souls, are that which I have attacked.

"I must confess, your majesty, that in the heat of controversy, I may have been overly vehement and unduly acrimonious. If such I have been, then I am indeed sorry for my zeal, but I cannot deny the basis of my attack upon this iniquitous system. I should say, however, that what I have written is not an attack upon the Holy Father. He is the head of the Church and, as such, deserving of our honor. It is an attack upon some of those counsellors with whom he has surrounded himself and who, I believe, in their zeal for monetary gain, have persuaded the Holy Father to do that which is not in accord with the will of God.

"This, I assume, is what I am expected to retract. If his

74

eminence, Father Eyk, can convince me from the Scriptures that I have been deceived, that I have erred in my interpretation of the teachings of the Bible, then I will be the first not only to retract but to cast the books which I have written into the fire."

The emperor had paid little attention to Martin's address for Luther had spoken in German; but he was keenly interested in the reactions of the people who thronged the hall to Martin's speech. He could readily see that the majority were arrayed on Martin's side. Some of the electors were also evidently back of Martin, and many of the Augustinian monks were with him as well.

When he had finished his address, Martin resumed his seat. Eyk took his place at the rostrum and began his attack. He sneered, "You have dodged the question which we propounded to you. To that question we want a plain and unequivocal reply."

Martin's address had been given calmly, dispassionately. But when Eyk demanded a "Yes" or "No" he was on his feet again.

Now, with deep earnestness and a smoldering fire in his heart, he addressed himself to the emperor: "Since your imperial majesty, and your highness, now assembled, require a plain, simple and brief answer, I will render one without reservation or evasion. Unless I shall be convinced by the testimony of Scripture, or by other and manifest reasons, (for upon the authority of popes and councils alone I cannot reply, since it is clear that they have often erred, and even contradicted one another,) I neither can nor will revoke anything that I have written, seeing that to act against conscience is neither safe nor honest. Here I stand: I can do no other. God help me! Amen!"

Thunderous applause greeted his last ringing statement. Eyk looked confused. The emperor was evidently impressed — not by Martin's words but by the response from the assemblage. He asked Martin to deliver the address in Latin.

"I did not understand a word of what you said when you spoke in your barbaric tongue," he explained.

It was somewhat difficult for Martin to give the address in Latin — not because Martin was not fluent in the tongue used by the Church, but because it was not easy to put into a speech in that language the same fervor with which he had spoken in German. It was after eight o'clock in the evening before Martin finished.

Following the meeting, Charles ordered the hall cleared of spectators and sent Martin into an anteroom, leaving only the official members of the diet in the hall with him.

There were those in the company which remained who insisted that Luther had been proven a heretic and, as such, was, therefore, subject to the death penalty.

"But I gave him a safe-conduct and it has not yet expired," the emperor objected.

"That safe-conduct would expire if he were proven guilty," one of the emperor's Italian advisers argued.

Duke George of Saxony immediately voiced his objection.

"The German princes will not endure the violation of a safe-conduct," he firmly asserted. "Such perfidy would arouse the entire nation against the empire."

Charles was a monarch without a conscience but he was also an exceedingly shrewd potentate. He had no desire to stir up trouble with his already troublesome German nobles. He listened carefully, therefore, when the elector of the Palatinate added sternly, "The death of Jan Huss has been the cause of too many calamities in Germany for us to think of again erecting a similar scaffold for the Wittenberg monk."

The emperor needed to cultivate the good will of these nobles; but it was also true that he needed to have the pope on his side. He therefore decided upon a course of action which would not antagonize the Germans but would be calculated to win the approval of the papacy. The pope had already declared that Martin Luther was a heretic. He would do likewise but he would not prescribe any form of punishment.

His mind made up, he summoned Martin back to the great hall for sentencing.

"It is our imperial decision," Charles announced, "that Martin Luther is a heretic. We, therefore, sentence him to banishment from our imperial presence. He can no longer fulfill the duties of his priesthood and shall be barred from observing the sacrament of the mass and all other sacraments of the Holy Church. Now, false monk, you will leave the court never to return."

This was, of course, a wholly innocuous decision. Martin had never before appeared in the imperial court; he had no intention of ever appearing before the emperor again, and the pope's excommunication had already decreed that he could not perform any of the sacraments, a prohibition which Martin had made no attempt to observe. The Italian ecclesiastics shook their heads in disappointment. They were well aware that a decree of banishment and excommunication meant nothing to Martin. The German nobles and those German clerics who counted themselves Martin's closest friends smiled. They knew that these decrees, high sounding as they were, would in no wise interfere with Martin's way of life.

They were confident that Martin would continue to teach in the University of Wittenberg. He would continue to preach in the parish church. The situation was unchanged. There existed still, all of the elements which might make for future conflict but they preferred it that way.

Martin was dismissed, the decree of banishment ringing in his ears. He spent several more days in Worms where he was visited by friends. Many of them commended him for his stand: others of a more timid nature sought to induce him to make his peace with the pope and the emperor.

Melancthon had joined the group by this time and sat in on these conferences.

"It is folly to expect Dr. Luther to back down," he informed the timid advisers. "He is confident that he has taken the right stand, and he will not depart from it one inch."

8

ON April 26th, 1521, Martin left Worms, accompanied by many of his friends and the armed escort which Frederick supplied him. Melancthon rode with him in his wagon. Most of the others went on horseback. Instead of retiring in disgrace, his return to Wittenberg became of the nature of a triumphal procession.

As far as most of the populace was concerned, they had decided that one of their own Germans had bested Italians and Spaniards and should be commended for his actions. Wherever he stopped, Martin was urged to preach in the churches. Crowds came to hear him and the people listened to him eagerly. He stopped briefly in Mohra, the town in which his father had spent his youth. Like his father, his kinfolk, whom he met there, were simple peasants and they treated him with marked consideration. No Luther had ever achieved such fame as had Hans Luther's son.

From Mohra Martin went on to Eisenach, the city which he greatly loved, and here the populace treated him as a conquering hero. After a brief stop here, he pressed on with only a few days remaining during which Martin would have the protection of the emperor's safe-conduct.

While Martin was thus journeying, the emperor, with the help of his advisers, was engaged in preparing a formal sentence for the crime of outlawry with which Martin, after leaving Worms, was charged. When the document was finally completed it was most thorough-going. Martin was adjudged guilty of crimes for which he had not even been charged in the formal hearing. Sentence was pronounced which claimed that Martin was guilty of being:

    1. A rebel against the Roman pontiff and the institution of the papacy.

2. A contumacious heretic.

3. A wretch who not only led a licentious life himself, but instructed others in license and a sensual life. Furthermore, he had openly defied all laws, whether of human or divine origin.

4. The very incarnate spirit of evil, which was all the more reprehensible in that said spirit was arrayed in the habiliments of the Augustinian friar.

In view of the imperial decree, it was announced that Martin was in rebellion against the empire and every subject of the emperor was charged with the responsibility of aiding in his apprehension and destruction.

The decree added that anyone who should be guilty of reading, printing or distributing any of Martin's writings, or who harbored him, aided, encouraged, or abetted him was likewise guilty of the same crimes as those with which he had been charged and would be subject to the same penalties as those which had been assessed against Martin.

Eight days after Martin had left Worms and after he had preached in both Mohra and Eisenach, as his small entourage was driving through a forest, Martin's wagon was set upon by a group of masked and armed horsemen. Yet, although Martin's horsemen were armed, they did not raise a hand to defend him.

Martin protested against the outrage with vehement language.

"You have no right to arrest me," he said. "I have here in my pouch the safe-conduct pledge of his majesty, the emperor. This safe-conduct has not yet expired."

None of the masked horsemen deigned to answer him. Instead, in silence, one of them seized the bridle of one of Martin's steeds and turned the carriage about so that it was headed back toward Eisenach.

Martin was sadly perplexed. He whispered to Philip, "I cannot understand why they do not assassinate me. Why are they taking us into custody? The emperor will have to release me."

Philip made no reply.

The wagon drove up to the ancient and strongly fortified castle of Wartburg.

Philip was told to descend from the wagon. One of the horsemen handed him the bridle of a horse. Philip mounted the steed. After bidding Martin farewell and advising him to be of good courage, he drove off in the direction of Wittenberg. Not a word was uttered concerning Martin's possible fate.

The whole situation puzzled Martin. Why was Philip released? And why had he been apprehended here? This was the Elector Frederick's province. How could it happen that Martin was arrested in the elector's territory, and especially in the very shadow of one of the elector's strongest fortifications?

When the wagon was stopped in the courtyard, one of the horsemen indicated to Martin that he should leave his conveyance. The horseman then dismounted and led Martin into the great hall of the castle. As Martin entered, he saw Frederick, his friend and protector, seated before a blazing fireplace.

With a smile, the elector remarked, "We have taken you prisoner, Dr. Luther. The emperor has decreed that you should be apprehended by any of his loyal subjects who might come upon you and, as you are well aware, he has no more loyal subject than Frederick of Saxony."

Martin could not believe his ears. The elector had been his friend and advocate in all of his troubles. At the recent trial he had thrown his influence to the side of Martin. Now apparently he had completely changed sides. Martin's face doubtless mirrored his consternation for the elector earnestly announced. "I know what you are thinking, Martin, but we have not deserted you. If we had allowed you to proceed along the highway to Wittenberg you would almost certainly be taken into custody by emissaries of the emperor. The only way to avoid having you fall into the hands of the emperor was to lay hold upon you before someone else did."

"But what do you intend to do with me?" Martin inquired.

"The only thing that we can do," the elector replied, "is to hold you here in the castle until it is deemed safe for you to leave. In the meantime you have much planning to do. In the eyes of both the Church and the empire you are a renegade, and there is a price on your head. But there are many of us who are committed heart and soul to the cause which you have espoused. Do you realize, Brother Martin," the elector added earnestly, "what the results of your stand will be?"

"What do you mean?" Martin inquired.

"You have actually been laying the foundations for a new church, reformed and purified, one which is based upon the teachings of holy Scriptures. We will help you build such a church, but for some time all must be done in secret. Your friends can come and go as you will that they shall, but for the present your safety depends upon your remaining here."

"A prisoner?" Martin asked.

"No, Brother Martin," the elector replied. "You are free to go now if you will, but our cause is lost if you leave here. Your safe-conduct is about to expire and the hands of many will be against you. Would you rather be here — a free man — or in some Spanish castle — a prisoner of the emperor?"

"Philip Melancthon was given a horse and allowed to depart," Martin said. "Was he aware of this plot?"

"He was not only aware of it but he approved most heartily," the elector assured him, "and he will be your means of contact with the outside world. But you must not regard yourself as a prisoner. If you stay here — and I hope that you will — you must know that you will be defended by a garrison which is completely loyal to us and to our cause and every man who has been chosen is ready to lay down his life for you."

Martin's friends, however, were greatly concerned when he did not return to Wittenberg, assuming that the emperor had broken his safe-conduct pledge and somehow disposed of him. Since only a few of them were aware that he had been lodged in Wartburg castle for his own safety, there was considerable furor when he failed to return to Wittenberg.

One of the older professors remarked, "It is the story of Jan Huss over again. One cannot put one's trust in princes."

Another remarked, "To whom can we now look for leadership if Dr. Luther is dead or imprisoned?"

That which was most puzzling to Martin's colleagues, however, was the attitude of Philip Melancthon. All of the members of the faculty had been cognizant of the respect and reverence which the young professor bore for Martin, but Philip seemed almost unconcerned about the failure of Martin to return from Worms.

Colleagues plied him with questions: "Where did Dr. Luther go? Was he apprehended and lodged in prison? Were his abductors some of the pope's hirelings or did they come from the emperor? Tell us what happened. If he is in prison we should make efforts to secure his release. You were with him when he was apprehended, were you not?"

"I was. Masked men set upon us soon after we had left Eisenach. They took Dr. Luther into captivity, but I managed to escape on horseback," Philip explained.

"But whose men were they?" one of the professors persisted.

81

"You saw them, did you not? Tell us. Were they sent by the pope or by the emperor?"

"I do not know. They were masked, as I said," Philip said.

"But what can we do for our brother?" one of the professors inquired. "Has the elector been apprised of Dr. Luther's arrest? Does he know what happened?"

"I suppose that he does," Philip acknowledged.

"Is he doing anything to secure *Herr* Luther's release?" the professor insisted.

"I do not know," Philip replied, adding drily, "His excellency has not seen fit to take me into his confidence."

It had been with considerable difficulty that Philip had dissembled, but the elector had impressed upon him the need for secrecy. "Dr. Luther's life may depend upon your discretion," he insisted.

At first Martin chafed under confinement, but the elector provided him with books and writing materials and Martin soon accustomed himself to the situation and spent his time writing. He became happier still when the elector sent him his Greek Testament.

"I shall arrange for the publication of whatever you write," the elector promised him. "In that way, although for a time you will be absent from the university, your voice will be heard through the printed page."

Martin, probably harking back to the experience of the Apostle John, author of the gospel which bears his name as well as the Book of Revelation, called his retreat at Wartburg, "Patmos," or "The Desert." At first he felt the irksomeness of confinement but finally became accustomed to it. He took advantage of the elector's offer and began to write.

His first pamphlet was called, "Tract On The Auricular Confession." In it he noted that the institution of the confession had been built up about dubious translations of a few Biblical verses. Although Martin was not fond of the epistle of James, which he called a "gospel of straw," he pointed out that a key verse, James 5:16, which had been used to bolster up the institution of the confessional, and which read, "Therefore confess your sins to one another, and pray for one another, that you may be healed," did not mean confession to a priest but the kind of confession which one Christian might make to another to lighten his burden of sin by sharing it with a kindred soul.

He followed this publication with a "Letter To The Students

82

Of Erfurt" in which he defined the place of the priesthood in the Church and pointed out that the priesthood of the Roman Church was not in accord with the Biblical position regarding the priesthood of believers.

Probably his most important work, however, was his exposure of the folly of monastic vows. In fact he went further than to define them as foolish: to him they were sinful. Thus he struck at the very center of the polity of the Roman Church.

The elector published the tracts and Melancthon saw to their distribution. Gradually Martin's friends came to understand that he had not been kidnapped by either pope or emperor, and they surmised that he was undoubtedly in a place of safety, but no hint as to his hiding place was divulged by either Philip or the elector.

During this period of confinement, Henry VIII came into the lists against Martin with the publication of his pamphlet on "The Treatise Of The Seven Sacraments." Martin had attacked the validity of five of the seven, leaving only baptism and the Lord's Supper. These two he regarded as genuine since they had been instituted by Jesus. It is doubtful, to be sure, if Henry wrote the treatise himself. Possibly his chaplain or an obscure priest in his court was the actual author of the treatise.

In order to insure its acceptance, however, it was published over the signature of the English monarch. The pope was so delighted with the treatise that, at a special consistory, he accorded a new title to the English monarch, one which all English monarchs have held to this day, "Defender of the Faith."

At the same time Henry had made his peace with Charles V, the emperor of the Holy Roman Empire, through the medium of Henry's secretary of state, Cardinal Wolsey, who had aspirations of becoming pope. Charles had led Wolsey to expect that the next time a vacancy existed in the papal office the whole influence of Spain and Germany would be exerted on his behalf in order to secure election to this high office.

Martin had a large apartment in the Wartburg castle and two attendants were assigned to him to minister to his needs. Occasionally, at the suggestion of the elector, he would sally forth from the castle for a walk or a ride.

The elector warned him of the danger of going forth alone, however, saying, "It would be wise always to go in the company of several people from the castle. You may be in no danger whatsoever, it is true, but I would rather that you did not take any chances."

Martin was restless, and these excursions from the castle helped him to overcome his restlessness. But the many letters which he wrote during the period of his sojourn in Wartburg gave evidence of the fact that he was yearning for a more active life than that of immolation in the castle.

One letter which described his sole hunting experience also indicated his pre-occupation with a personal devil who was as real an adversary to Martin as was the pope. He wrote:

> Last week I hunted for two days to see what the bitter-sweet pleasure of heroes was like. We took two hares and a few poor partridges — a worthy occupation indeed for men with nothing to do. I even moralized among the snares and dogs, and the superficial pleasure I may have derived from the hunt was equalled by the pity and pain which are a necessary part of it. It is an image of the devil hunting innocent little creatures with his guns and his hounds, the impious magistrates, bishops and theologians.
>
> I deeply felt this parable of the simple and faithful soul. A still more cruel parable followed. With great pains I saved a little live rabbit and rolled it up in the sleeve of my coat, but when I left it and went a little way off, the dogs found the poor rabbit and killed it by biting its right leg and throat through the cloth. Thus do the Pope and Satan rage to kill souls and are not stopped by my labor.
>
> I am sick of this kind of hunting and prefer to chase bears, wolves, foxes, and that sort of wicked magistrate with spear and arrow. It consoles me to think that the mystery of salvation is near, when hares and innocent creatures will be captured rather by men than by bears, wolves, and hawks, i.e., the bishops and theologians.

The rigors of his monastic life in previous years finally caught up with Martin during this period and he was frequently ill and depressed. He had laid aside the robes of his order but he could not as easily lay aside the habits of living which he had developed. Accompanying his depression he frequently suffered from indigestion and, since he often overworked, from nervous irritation and exhaustion. Added to this was calculus, the formation of stones in his bladder. The chief cause of his worry and anxiety, to be sure, was his fear that his disappearance might seem an indication of cowardice. He felt that, with so much happening out in the active arena of the university, he should be in the midst of the battle.

The letters which he wrote were all to friends and colleagues, but he made one exception. When the archbishop of Mayence, made bold by Martin's disappearance, began the sale of indulgences, Martin wrote the ecclesiastic such a scathing letter that the cleric immediately desisted.

There was one especially important task which Martin was able to accomplish — the translation of the New Testament into the German tongue. Martin's was not the first such translation, but all previous attempts to translate the Bible had been from the Latin Vulgate. Luther chose to translate the New Testament from the original Greek of Erasmus' edition. He had become a very able Greek scholar and his command of his native tongue was remarkable. He avoided stilted expressions and chose the simple speech of the home and market place. He not only gave the Germans a great translation but he actually molded the German tongue into an idiom which would be used by the great authors of the country in generations to come.

Having completed this work, he would probably have gone on to still other translation work if it had not been for news which came to him from Wittenberg. His good friend Carlstadt, having broken, as Martin did, from Rome, went much farther in his disagreement with the papacy than did Martin. To Martin's mind Carlstadt and his followers were going too far, too fast.

Therefore, early in March 1522, after ten months' absence, Martin reappeared on the campus of the university. The elector had agreed with him that he should return. "Matters are getting out of hand," he said. "It is time that you were back in Wittenberg to guide our people."

Martin was joyously received, but there were those, of course, who were not so happy to see him return. Carlstadt was one of these. He had aspired to leadership in the movement which Martin had inaugurated, and never forgot the fact that Martin had to rescue him from ignominious defeat in the debate with Eck. Luther returned to the university as a hero but also as a champion whom some, who had ostensibly been his followers, resented.

9

*I*T should not be forgotten that it was never the intention of Martin Luther to divide the Church. He loved the Church, respected the papal office, and believed that the Church should be preserved intact. He recognized the fact that church leaders were as fallible as he knew himself to be, that priests were sinners who still had the capacity to become saints. If Martin had a hero in the New Testament aside from his Saviour Jesus Christ it was the Apostle Paul, and Paul, in speaking of those who lacked many of the qualities needed for perfection, mentioned "sinners of whom I am chiefest." If Paul so regarded himself, how, then, could Martin Luther consider himself to be perfect? How could any human pope regard himself as being without sin, or how could the Church so regard any one of them?

Martin didn't expect perfection of popes or prelates and was prepared to accept their leadership and direction as long as their motives were right. But the motivation for the sale of indulgences had been so thoroughly crass and selfish that Martin had perforce to protest it. Yet as he made his protest, he had believed that, when the matter was called to the attention of the pope, the holy father would immediately set about to remedy it. When the pope not only failed to correct this abuse but actually defended the practice Martin had felt impelled to speak out.

Differing from Martin, Carlstadt was ready to change the Church completely. Martin had spoken out against the sin of offering homage to images in the churches: Carlstadt insisted that they would have to be thrown out of the churches, pictures and statues alike. Martin had an innate love for the beautiful and an earnest respect for the past. Many of the pictures commemorated great events of ages which were gone. He felt that visible representa-

86

tions of passages in the life of the Saviour and the apostles could be used to good advantage in reminding people, by visual means, of the courage of the Master and His apostles.

The greatest difference of opinion between Martin and Carlstadt came, however, in their thinking concerning the celebration of the Lord's Supper. Carlstadt threw the celebration of the Supper and participation in it open to everyone. In contrast, also, to the solemn and stately celebration of a mass it had become in his ministration altogether commonplace. Martin believed that only those who had demonstrated and professed a real faith in the Lord Jesus Christ should be admitted to the Supper: Carlstadt opened the doors to everyone without preparation of any kind and without inquiring into the faith and character of the participants.

There was another vital difference in Luther's and Carlstadt's thinking concerning the character of the Lord's Supper as well.

"Carlstadt rejects the presence of Christ in the Holy Supper," Martin remarked to Melancthon. "If, therefore, one accepts his thesis what is the Supper?"

"But, Dr. Luther, you have told me that you yourself do not believe that the bread and wine actually become the body and blood of our Saviour when blessed by a priest. You have rejected that view of the nature of the Eucharist," Melancthon reminded him.

"Of course," Martin affirmed. "No words of a priest could transform bread into the actual body of our Lord, wine into His veritable blood, but I do insist that when a sincere believer partakes in faith of the Holy Supper, with the consumption of bread and wine, he also partakes of Jesus' sufferings upon Calvary. As far as Carlstadt is concerned, he has made the eucharist cheap and meaningless."

Martin had expected that he might be hounded by representatives of the papacy but he discovered upon his reappearance in Wittenberg that he had little to fear from them. For one reason, in the closing months of 1521, Leo had died. Elected as his successor was Adrian, the cardinal of Utrecht. Before his election Adrian had indicated that he was thoroughly out of sympathy with the practice of selling indulgences and with other programs which had given the Church its bad reputation among the more spiritually-minded members of the clergy.

He had no intention of persecuting a monk who had disagreed with Leo's program; and he very earnestly sought to purge the Church of its evils which had grown up in the past. Hence Martin was in no danger from the pope. But the prelates who surrounded Adrian were not interested in reform, and Adrian discovered that if he attempted to push through the reforms, the need for which he recognized, he would be considered as one who gave comfort to a man who was now regarded as a renegade monk. Certainly that monk had broken one cardinal principle of his brotherhood: he had failed to render the obedience to his superiors which was an essential part of the practices of the priesthood.

Nor was the Reformation movement, once started, capable of being halted. It had also assumed political overtones. The empire, although it was still ostensibly a single unit, was also split into various parts. The German nobles had no desire to render obedience to the emperor. They were suspicious of Italian and Spanish domination and watched with eager expectancy the growth of the movement under Martin Luther.

When Adrian decided to publish a bull in which he would express his detestation for the misuse of indulgences, he found his hands tied by his counselors. Adrian believed that indulgences were necessary and justified, that they helped to release sinners from a feeling of hopelessness. He had no intention of condemning the practice of granting them: he was concerned only with doing away with the abuses which had grown up with the system.

While the pope contemplated this problem, Martin continued his attacks upon the papacy. He was actually choosing a mistaken target since Adrian was as eager for reform as he was. His target should have been the cardinals for, with contempt for the reformer on the papal throne, they continued to pursue their own course of amassing money, leaving the pope to regret his elevation to the papacy.

In the meantime, Martin continued with programs and pronouncements which widened still further the division between himself and Rome. In a letter which Martin wrote and which he entitled, "Address To The Nobility Of The German Nation," he came out strongly for the marriage of parish priests. Such marriages, to his way of thinking, were advisable for the priests in view of the fact that celibacy had actually not been practiced by them. This oftentimes created scandals among them.

At this time he did not advocate marriage for members of the monastic orders who, he felt, were in a different category from the members of the clergy who ministered to individual parishes.

Within a short time, however, he changed his mind and advocated marriage for monks and nuns as well as parish priests. He had no intention of getting married himself. In fact, all of the monks had left the cloister in Wittenberg except two, Martin Luther and one other. Many of the monks went into some secular employment after they were married. And, although he felt that they should not have married, Martin became active in finding wives for as many of the brothers as desired to be married — and most of them did.

Philip chided him one day for failing to consider marriage for himself.

"You have become a veritable match-maker," he said, "but remain a bachelor. Why do you not choose some young woman, marry her and raise a family?"

Martin smiled.

"I will confess to you, my friend, what I would probably not confess to any other," he replied. "I have renounced the vow of celibacy, it is true, and feel no longer bound by it. But, having lived the celibate life so long, I am probably afraid to launch into family life. I am now forty years of age, you see, and it is difficult for me to change my ways."

"But as long as you remain celibate, you cast a reflection upon those who have left that way of life," Philip dared to tell him.

"No," Martin replied, shaking his head. "I do not think that I can be criticized on that score. I have given encouragement to all the brothers and to the nuns; but I am like Paul, I suspect, and do not consider marriage because it would interfere with my ministry."

"It cannot be that, Brother Martin," Philip countered. "Paul was an itinerant. Your ministry is here in Wittenberg. You still have a settled home in the monastery and if you married you would merely move out of it into your own home."

"Patience, Philip," Martin replied. "If I should find the woman who would have me to husband, I may still be married."

Even as they were holding their discussion, however, events were conspiring to open the way for Martin into wedded life. On January 29th 1499, a daughter had been born to Hans von Bora and his wife who lived in a little town south of Leipzig. The daughter had been named Catherine and the name, for convenience' sake, had been promptly shortened to Katie.

When Katie was five years old, her mother died. Her father married again soon afterward and decided to put Katie in a convent in the expectation that she would eventually become a nun. Entering upon that life meant that Katie was shut off from the outside world. Her days were spent in prayer, study and learning to do works of charity. At the age of sixteen she became a nun. Prior to that time she had not been out of the convent since the day that she had entered it; but, having taken the vows, she could now go out into the town, accompanied always by a sister nun, to visit the homes of the poor.

She had almost forgotten what life was like on the outside, and at first she was shocked at what she saw in the little town of Grimma. Eventually she became accustomed to the world outside the convent but if she longed to have a part in it she gave no indication of such a desire. She was a faithful, obedient, consecrated nun.

Then came the new movement in Germany. The peace of the convent was shattered. Priests were being married. The services in the churches were being changed. Some of the nuns began to talk among themselves about the possibility of marriage.

Margaret Zeschau remarked to Katie, "Why should we not marry also if the priests do?"

Katie was horrified.

"We have taken a vow of celibacy. You would not have us break that vow, would you?" she asked.

"Dr. Luther has said that it was wrong to take such a vow," Margaret replied. "If one desired to remain virgin this is no reason why one should not, he has said, but to take such a vow as a religious act he feels is wrong."

Katie pondered the idea. Soon she found that other nuns were discussing the matter quietly among themselves. Eventually they decided to go to the mother superior and request her counsel.

Ave von Schonfeld was the boldest one among them. She was chosen, therefore, to act as their spokesman.

"Mother," she said, "word has reached us that nuns all over Germany are leaving their convents and are being married. When are we to be free to do the same?"

The mother superior set her lips grimly.

"Never!" she replied. "If all other convents fall into sin ours will not. I forbid any of you even to consider such carnal ideas. They spring out of the heresies of that mad monk, Luther, and his followers."

The nuns, in a rebellious mood, went back to their cells. From that time on they discovered that they were virtually in captivity. Later, one of them managed to smuggle out word of their desire to escape, and on the night of April 4th, 1523, three men came to the convent in Grimma and assisted twelve of the younger nuns to escape. The older sisters had no desire to leave but they made no attempt to dissuade the younger women, nor did they put any impediments in their way. The mother superior heard no noise, so quiet were they, and they managed to escape into the night.

A few days later the men brought the nuns to Martin, leaving the responsibility for their welfare in his hands. Martin explained their situation to George Spalatin in a letter. He wrote:

Wittenberg, April 10, 1523

Grace and peace. Nine fugitive nuns, a wretched crowd, have been brought to me by honorable citizens of Torgau. I mean Leonard Copps and his nephew, Wolf Tomitzsch; there is, therefore, no cause for suspicion. I pity them much, but most of all the others who are dying everywhere in such numbers in their cursed and impure celibacy. This sex, so very, very weak, joined by nature or rather by God to the other, perishes when cruelly separated. O tyrants! O cruel parents and kinsmen in Germany! O popes and bishops, who can curse you enough? Who can sufficiently execrate the blind fury which has taught and enforced such things? But this is not the place to do it.

You ask what I shall do with them? First, I shall inform their relatives and ask them to support the girls; if they will not I shall have the girls otherwise provided for. Some of the families have already promised me to take them; for some I shall get husbands, if I can. The names of these nuns are: Magdalene von Staupitz, Elsa von Canitz, Ave Gross, Ave von Schonfeld and Catherine von Bora. Here they are, who serve Christ, in need of true pity. They have escaped from the cloister in miserable condition. I pray you also do the work of charity and beg some money for me from your rich courtier, by which I can support the girls a week or two until their kinsmen or others provide for them . . .

The poor, who would willingly give, have nothing; the rich either refuse or give so reluctantly that they lose the credit of the gift with God and take up my time begging for them. Nothing is too much for the world and its way. Of my annual salary I have only ten or fifteen gulden left, besides which not a penny has been given me by my brothers or by the city. But I ask them for nothing, to emulate the boast of Paul, despoiling other churches to serve my Corinthians free . . .

Farewell and pray for me,   MARTIN LUTHER

Martin searched high and low through Wittenberg, seeking to find places for the nine nuns. One, however, was taken in by relatives in her home town of Grimma. There was, therefore, one less for whom provision needed to be made. Martin found a teaching post for another. Others were taken into home of relatives. There were still three for whom Martin had found no refuge. Katie von Bora was one of these.

At a conference with Philip Melancthon, Martin confessed to his young friend that he had fallen in love with Ave von Schonfeld.

"Although she is much younger than I am, I believe that I could win her heart," he confessed.

"I am happy to hear that you have decided to be married," Philip responded warmly. "She is a fortunate woman who would get you for a husband. Too, you will be a sympathetic, warm-hearted father. I know that from personal experience for you have been more than a father to me."

"Do you think that Ave could love me?" Martin asked.

Smiling, Philip replied, "If she knows you as well as I do, she would at least learn to love you; and I believe that she would eagerly accept your proffer of marriage. But then," he added, shaking his head, "I really know nothing about women, so I cannot say for certain whether or no she would consider marrying you."

"You are most encouraging," Martin wryly remarked.

However, he soon discovered what the answer to his proposal was to be. Ave made it plain that she could not consider marrying him.

"I love you as a father and benefactor," she said, "but I had never even given a thought to marriage until I left the convent, and now I have made up my mind that if I do marry, the man whom I choose should be one more nearly my own age."

Martin realized that his cause was hopeless. Ave's reply was so forthright and positive that there seemed to be no possibility that she would change her mind. Then, within a very short time, Ave and her sister Margaret were married, neither of them to former priests, and they and their husbands moved away from Wittenberg. Katie von Bora was the only one of the former nuns who remained in Wittenberg.

Martin asked Katie what her plans for the future were.

"I have made no plans except to remain here," she told him.

"Would it not be advisable for you to return to your home?" he inquired.

"No," she said. "I was placed in the convent when I was a mere child because my stepmother did not want to be bothered with me. If I were to return to my home it would merely cause trouble. She certainly would not want me. It is much better that I remain here."

"Then I must try to find a husband worthy enough to join you in matrimony," Martin suggested.

Tartly she replied, "Dr. Luther, I am quite capable of finding my own husband. Please do not trouble yourself about me."

"But I feel responsible," he replied. "After all, none of you would have left your convent if I had not criticized the papacy for permitting the sale of indulgences, if I had not begun a reformation movement within the Church."

"I am provided for," she sturdily insisted. "*Herr* Bauer has asked me to live in his home, doing the housekeeping and looking after his little children."

"That is good," Martin said, nodding his head. "He is a fine man. Perhaps he may want to marry you. After all, his wife has been dead for several years."

Katie's face flushed.

"Dr. Luther, pray do not concern yourself," she retorted sharply. "I respect *Herr* Bauer. He is a fine man. But if I were ever to marry it would not be to him."

Within the space of a year Katie became known throughout Wittenberg for her kind deeds and continual aid to the poor. *Herr* Bauer remarked one day to Martin, "She is truly a jewel, and have you heard what our neighbors have begun to call her?"

Puzzled, Martin replied, "I don't think that I have. What is she called?"

With a broad smile, *Herr* Bauer replied, "St. Catherine of Siena."

"Undoubtedly she well deserves it," Martin replied.

Soon after they had had this conversation, it appeared as if Martin's search for a husband for Katie had ended. Philip had engaged as an assistant in his department at the university, a young man named Jerome Baumgartner who had come from Nuremberg. Jerome had graduated from the university in 1521. After his graduation he had been away from Wittenberg for two years and then had returned to serve under Philip Melancthon.

Jerome became interested in Katie and within a year the two were betrothed. Martin was happy for Katie's sake but at the same time he had an empty feeling in his heart. He had become interested in her welfare but, without realizing it, the interest had become more than casual. Katie was not beautiful but she was essentially a very cheerful person with a warm, friendly manner. Certainly she had neither the bodily form nor the classic features of Ave von Schonfeld with whom Martin had earlier fallen in love.

During this period, Martin began an intellectual controversy with Desiderius Erasmus, one of the great scholars of his time and one who had inspired Martin Luther in many ways. Erasmus had prepared the Greek New Testament which Martin had used in translating the Bible into the German vernacular and had left the Roman priesthood in 1493 after he had taken holy orders the year before.

In 1517, when Martin began his controversy with the Roman Church, Erasmus had been one of the first to applaud the movement. However, Erasmus had no desire to leave the Church as Luther had done.

On one occasion Martin remarked to Philip, "The man is the greatest scholar of our time but he has no sound conviction or, if he does, I have never discovered it. He blows hot and cold. First he is a critic of the Church and then he becomes an apologist for it."

Martin came to feel that Erasmus would have become a reformer and would have joined with Martin if he had not feared the consequences of taking such a step. In any event Luther was thoroughly disappointed with Erasmus. Actually his criticism was not altogether just. Erasmus was basically a scholar. He preferred the quiet of his study to the turmoil of the arena, and was fearful of becoming embroiled in such a movement as Martin had initiated. He also believed sincerely that the Church could have been reformed from within.

Martin had other disappointments which also troubled him. He was a turbulent individual himself and not averse to controversy, but at the same time, as is often true of tempestuous people, he had an extremely sensitive soul. Staupitz had been one of his warmest friends in the clergy and it greatly disturbed Martin when the former couldn't go all the way with him out of the Roman Church.

The third great disappointment was Professor Carlstadt. Carlstadt had been one of the first Wittenberg professors to espouse the Reformation movement, but he had gone off on what Martin considered a tangent. So Martin felt very much alone. There was also something of an empty feeling in his heart when, in 1524, he finally put aside his monk's habit and began to wear ordinary clothing.

Coupled with these disappointments was one which he had accepted as his own although it was really Katie's. Jerome Baumgartner had left Wittenberg with the understanding that he would return to the city to marry Katie, but time passed and he not only did not return but he also failed to write to her. Months went by and she had no word from the young professor who had pledged his troth to her. Finally she decided that he had changed his mind and hesitated to inform her of the fact.

However, it looked as if Katie's problems were solved when Dr. Herman Glatz confided to Martin that he loved Katie and was eager to marry her.

"Would she have me for a husband, do you suppose?" Glatz inquired of Martin.

"I'm sure I don't know," Martin replied. "Why don't you ask her?"

Glatz hesitantly confided, "I find it hard to express myself . . . You are a good friend of hers and her confidant . . . and I thought that perhaps you . . ."

". . . would act as your emissary," said Martin, adding the concluding phrase to Dr. Glatz' sentence.

"Well, yes," Dr. Glatz admitted.

"It would be better if you would plead your own cause," Martin suggested.

Actually Martin was not particularly fond of Glatz. He was convinced that the doctor was an individual with little force of character, although he had to admit that the man was in truth a capable scholar. He agreed, nevertheless, that he would represent his fellow professor in seeking Katie's hand.

He postponed the mission as long as he could since he could not in honesty enthusiastically press the professor's suit. Finally he decided that he had let too much time elapse and resolved to call on Katie at once. He found it difficult to know just how to broach the subject. Very haltingly, therefore, he began.

"You know Katie, how deeply concerned I have been for your welfare," he remarked tentatively.

"Yes, Dr. Luther," Katie agreed.

"I was greatly disappointed when Jerome broke his promise to marry you," he added.

"It was probably for the best," Katie remarked, shrugging her shoulders. "I think that he was too young to know his own mind."

"Then, perhaps, you would consider marriage with an older man," Martin suggested slyly.

"Do you know such an one?" she inquired.

"I do," Martin said confidently. "He has come to me avowing his love for you and asking me to represent him and press his suit."

Drily Katie replied, "If he were a man he would come himself."

"Well, but he is timid," Martin said.

"Then tell me the name of this paragon," Katie countered. "Do I know him?"

"I'm sure you do. He is Dr. Herman Glatz," Martin replied. "He is a very brilliant scholar indeed."

"Dr. Luther, when I marry it will not be to a man merely because he is reputed to be a brilliant scholar," Katie retorted hotly. "And as for Dr. Glatz, I would not marry him if he and I were the only two people in the world."

Meditatively she added, "However, Dr. Luther, if you would bring me an offer of marriage from one other man, one who is a profound scholar, who has never married, but is also a strong and kindly man, I would say 'Yes,' to his proposal."

"Do you have some one person in mind?" Martin asked.

"I do," she announced boldly. "I mean you, Martin Luther."

Martin flushed to the roots of his hair.

"I have a conference with Dr. Melancthon," he said hurriedly. "You think over Dr. Glatz' proposal."

"Never!" she said emphatically.

Martin hurried away from the Bauer home, his mind in a whirl. Having sought the hand of Ave von Schonfeld he did not think that he could consider marrying another, but why not Katie? She was a good woman. She had proved her courage in escaping from the convent and taking what was basically a menial job, that of housekeeper in the Bauer home.

Also, Martin had to acknowledge to himself that he loved this girl, but did he really want to be married, or was he still unconsciously bound by the vow of celibacy which he had been urging others, monks and nuns alike, to break?

He decided that he would talk this matter over with Philip Melancthon. Philip would give him good advice. However, when it came to the business of confiding such a delicate matter to his friend, he found that it was difficult to do so. He began on several occasions and then each time changed the subject.

"What is the matter with you, Dr. Luther?" Philip inquired one day. "You have been going about this past week as if you were in a fog."

"Nothing at all," Martin replied testily. "I feel fine."

A week later Martin returned to the Bauer home, timid as a schoolboy. He was glad that the children were not underfoot when he arrived and that Dr. Bauer was away.

He had scarcely had time to take off his cloak when, with his usual forthrightness, he blurted forth his proposal of marriage. "Would you have me as your husband, Katie?" he asked. "I know now that I love you, that I have loved you since the first time I saw you."

Katie smiled enigmatically.

"Since I first laid eyes upon you, since I first heard you preach, I had hoped that some day you would ask that question," she said quietly, her face alight with gentle affection.

She is truly beautiful, Martin decided.

"And when will you marry me?" Martin eagerly asked.

"As soon as we make the arrangements," she said.

10

WITHIN a few days Martin and Katie were secretly married.
The wedding over, Martin announced enthusiastically to his
wife, "Now we must prepare for a proper celebration so that everyone may share our joy. I shall want my parents to come and you
will want to invite your family and friends."

"Your people must come," Katie said, "but I feel that I have no
family. I told you, Martin, that my stepmother hated me and, in
order to get rid of me, placed me in the convent when I was only
a child. Nor did she or my father ever visit me there. You are my
only family, Dr. Luther, until we have children of our own."

Martin smiled.

"You must drop the 'doctor' now, Katie dear," he said gently.
"I am from henceforth plain Martin to you."

"No," she said, "you will always be Dr. Luther to me. I love
you as Dr. Luther and I shall always want to be obedient to you
and revere you."

"But between wife and husband . . ." Martin began.

"We are different from other wives and husbands," Katie said.

"Yes, I suppose so," Martin said reluctantly, "but still . . ."

"It is settled, Dr. Luther," Katie said.

In preparation for the wedding celebration, Martin moved out
of the monastery, thereby cutting off the last tie which bound him
to the Church. At the same time he laid aside the vestments to
which he had become so thoroughly accustomed and attired himself
in the garb of an ordinary citizen. He had become so used to a
monk's habit, however, that his clothing was as somber as the habit
which he had put aside.

The wedding celebration was held on June 27, 1525. The
home to which they planned to move was too small, however, for

the host of people who were invited to the wedding breakfast. The celebration lasted for several days and was held in the monastery which Martin thought he had left for all time. The host of people who came included most of the faculty of the university, Martin's parents, the elector of Saxony, and those former monks who were still resident in Wittenberg.

If there were those who approved Martin's nuptials, there were more who disapproved. Even some of his friends criticized him, and by his marriage he put a potent weapon into the hands of the bishops and cardinals who had opposed his reforms. He was accused of the most vile crimes. Basically, to be sure, the charge was the principal one that Martin had broken with the Church in order that he might also break his vows of celibacy and that he might gratify his own passions.

He was accused of having fathered other children during the years when he had been a priest. "At last we have unmasked the evil within this renegade man's soul," some said. He was accused by others of being antichrist, of bearing the mark of the beast on his forehead as mentioned in the Book of Revelation.

To his friend Spalatin he wrote sorrowfully, realizing as he did so that Spalatin could not possibly answer his epistle, however he felt concerning one of his former monks. Yet Martin felt a need to unburden himself to one who had once been his father-confessor. He wrote:

> I have made myself so cheap and despised by this marriage, that I expect the angels laugh and the devils weep thereat. The world and its wise men have not yet seen how pious and sacred is marriage, but they consider it impious and devilish in me. It pleases me, however, to have my marriage condemned by those who are ignorant of God.

So many people now began to throng Martin's new home that, at the suggestion of the elector, he decided to move back into the Black Cloister. Since all the monks had left it to join the Reformation movement it had been completely vacated and the elector could see no reason why Martin and Katie should not occupy it.

"It is much nearer to the parish church also," the elector said, "and our people want you to be their pastor as well as a professor. You are aware, I am sure, that the pulpit affords you an opportunity to proclaim your faith which might be lacking if you remained in the classroom and spoke only to students."

Katie was happy also to occupy the cloister and she quickly transformed it into a comfortable home for the two. A large room was set aside for Martin's study and it was daily thronged with people from other parts of Germany as well as townfolk from Wittenberg.

Martin now began to understand that, once embarked on reformation, he was to be sought for advice upon all manner of questions. The immediately pressing problem confronting him was how to set up an educational program for Germany, and, in addition, what the relationship between the people and the government should be, and how far and in what direction reformation should go.

One of his first acts after his wedding, was to address a letter to the councils in the various cities of Germany concerning the schools which were located within their boundaries. He entitled it, "A Letter to the Aldermen and Cities of Germany on the Erection and Maintenance of Christian Schools." Martin believed that the curriculum of the schools should include the teaching of religion as well as instruction in the three R's. Children everywhere should be taught how to read the Bible and also the studies which would train them to govern their fellows.

The reformation movement which he had begun, had taken the schools out of the hands of the Catholic Church in those areas where the movement had spread, but Martin continued to believe in the principle that the Church should be engaged in the whole process of education. The only difference between the conduct of the schools when the state religion was Roman Catholic and now that it had become Reformed was the manner in which religion should be taught.

Undoubtedly Martin was responsible, even though he failed to realize it, for the widespread and serious uprising of the peasants in 1525. The revolt would probably never have begun had Luther not challenged papal authority and the authority of the prelates, but if these could be challenged with impunity, why could not the nobles be similarly challenged? The leader of the peasants' revolt was Thomas Munzer and his avowed aim was to ameliorate the lot of the peasant class.

Martin recognized the fact that the plight of the common people was dire. He himself had come from peasant stock and he knew from personal experience how little the farmers, the miners, and others who comprised the working class received for their labors, how little they had with which to pay for the ordinary necessities of life; but Munzer was a fanatic in whom a religious zeal was blended with a passion for social reform. Munzer encouraged the peasants to seize the towns of Thuringia, depose the magistrates, and compel all persons, upon pain of death, to put aside all laces and furbelows. Everyone should be simply attired as were the common people. All members of the nobility were to be compelled to renounce their titles.

At the same time Munzer injected a religious note into the controversy by setting up Anabaptist cells within all of the towns of the province. These were actually churches, governed congregationally. Baptism by immersion was a prerequisite to membership. At the outset of the rebellion, the elector of Saxony paid little attention to the movement since it had originated in another province, but it finally became such a serious threat to the government of his province and adjacent states that, in conjunction with the duke of Brunswick and the landgrave of Hesse-Homburg, he raised an army to oppose the undisciplined hordes which were seizing the cities of those independent states.

Before taking the field against them, however, Frederick attempted conciliation. He promised the rebels that they would not be punished for their insurrection if they would return peacefully to their homes, and he further agreed that he would give them prompt relief from the iniquities of the land rental system under which they cultivated their farms, and from the low wage scale for their labor in the mines. Frederick the Wise was a generous man with a keen appreciation of the injustices under which they labored, and he undoubtedly recognized the fact there were just causes for complaint. However, he sensed also that their revolution posed a threat to all forms of civil government and was resolved to suppress it. Martin Luther joined with the elector in urging the peasants to accept the latter's terms.

It was all to no avail. Munzer scornfully rejected the proffer of peace and continued to urge the peasants to carry on with their revolt. In the meantime, the elector died and was succeeded by his brother John. Anxious to spare the revolutionaries the horrors of war, John dispatched one of the members of his staff, a young nobleman, to confer with them, with an offer of pardon to all the insurgents on condition that they immediately lay down their arms.

The plight of the insurgents was desperate. It was a generous offer since they were surrounded by troops. The rebels had barricaded themselves in Frankenhausen but they could readily discern the ranks of the soldiers who surrounded their village.

The peasant group was an unorganized mob. They had only one leader, Thomas Munzer, who was in absolute authority. However, some of the peasants went to him to urge him to capitulate. "It is folly to continue the battle," their spokesmen said. "The elector and other princes have us bottled up. Better to yield now than engage in a battle which we are sure to lose."

As they were conferring, there was a sudden downpour of rain although the sun was still shining between banks of clouds. The banner which the peasants had adopted was a white flag with a rainbow emblazoned on it. As they parleyed, a rainbow suddenly appeared in the sky.

"Oh, ye of little faith!" Munzer shouted. "If you lack faith in me have faith in God's sign. Behold who is on our side! God has sent us a sign that our just cause will be victorious. Why should we fear when God is with us? Are you cowards that you will not fight for The Eternal? See the pledge which God has given us that we will be victorious. That is His promise that the wicked nobles will be utterly destroyed."

This was all that was needed to set off the mob. They fell upon the unhappy envoy, and in sight of the troops, hacked him to pieces, mingling execrations with hymns. In a matter of minutes the man was dead, his head impaled upon a spear and waved aloft. In shocked horror the elector ordered his troops to do battle but the peasants began their attack even before the troops sought to engage them.

Fanatically the peasants flung themselves upon the troops which had ringed them in. Shouting imprecations and singing their praises of Almighty God, they attacked the ranks of soldiers. The troops far outnumbered them, but they were confident that God would intervene on their behalf to do battle with the soldiers.

Of eight thousand peasants who had thrown themselves into battle before the day's end more than five thousand were slain. Munzer, attempting to flee from the holocaust, was captured and condemned to death in a court convened by the elector and other nobles right on the battlefield.

The revolt was over but the seeds of revolt had been sown all over Germany. The majority of nobles by this time had espoused the Lutheran cause. As yet there was no organized Lutheran Church. Martin's adherents, and Martin himself, confidently expected that eventually peace would be made with the papacy. But gradually they came to realize that a new church was in the making.

During this period Martin's character began to change. He had been brave, but inclined to doubt his own abilities, inclined to periods of moodiness. Katie was a very practical wife and bolstered up Martin's faith in himself. He plunged into his work with renewed vigor and joy. When he was inclined to periods of despondency, Katie went about her household tasks with a song on her lips.

On one occasion Martin had been brooding for several days. Reports still came of groups of peasants in revolt, of increased papal pressure on the nobles to renounce their stand for Luther. These conspired to make him feel that he had undertaken a hopeless task.

On the morning when he was most deeply melancholic he came into the dining room for breakfast. Katie greeted him, attired in a black dress which was as funereal in appearance as the costume which she had worn as a nun. Martin glanced at her quizzically. She usually greeted him with a cheerful, *"Guten morgen, Herr Dokter,"* but this morning she said not a word.

"What is wrong, Katie?" Martin inquired.

"God is dead," she announced sadly.

"Woman, that is a terrible heresy. God is not dead nor doth He sleep. Never say that The Eternal has died. When heaven and earth shall pass away God will remain," he affirmed.

"Then why do you waken each morning with such a doleful expression on your face? Why go through the day sighing like the north wind? In your university classes you claim to interpret the mind of God. You have appeared to know Him well; and I became certain, from the expression on your face, that God must surely have expired."

She made this statement without a change of expression. Suddenly Martin burst out laughing.

"You have convinced me, Katie dear," he said. "So, if ever you see me again with a melancholy countenance, remind me that God is living, that He will live forevermore. I promise you that I shall try not to appear as dour as a shriveled turnip."

Thereupon Martin seized his wife in an exuberant hug and kissed her soundly on her cheek.

Katie pretended shocked surprise.

"Dr. Luther!" she protested.

Thereafter, if Martin was troubled by doubts, he avoided bringing his problems to breakfast or dinner. Nor did Katie surprise him again in a disconsolate mood. If he had difficulties, he kept them to himself.

Luther's world was a troubled one but Martin and Katie seemed to be living on an island of safety. Excommunicated by both pope and emperor, Martin's life should have been in peril. To have made the interdict against him, effective troops should have been sent to Wittenberg to take the reformer prisoner, but the troops were never dispatched. In the meantime, Germany became more and more protestant as Martin's teachings became more widespread.

Wittenberg became a seat of Protestant learning. Frederick had founded the university, intending that it should become a seat of learning similar to other universities. Its various faculties grew and the student body increased in size but the fame of the institution was due to the lectures and teaching of its most controversial figure, Martin Luther, ably assisted by Philip Melancthon.

Furthermore, the emperor and the pope were in constant controversy. There was trouble in the east with the Turks. The emperor had difficulties with France. There was no way to reach Germany except through France and the emperor knew that before a force sufficient to handle the rebellious German provinces could ever reach the Rhine they would be stopped by French forces.

In addition, Henry VIII, who had been given the awe-inspiring title of "Defender of the Faith," wanted to divorce Katherine of Aragon. If she had been an ordinary person this might have been arranged, but she had been a Spanish princess, and the Emperor Charles could not be persuaded that such a divorce should be arranged.

For this reason, Martin was unmolested by either emissaries of the emperor or the pope. The emperor held frequent diets but their pronouncements made no impression upon the German princes. Furthermore, the Elector John had openly espoused the cause of the Reformation and had become a warm personal friend of Martin. Martin's communications with the Elector Frederick had been by letter; his communications with John were held face to face.

Indeed, John met frequently with the controversial Martin. He coveted Martin's advice and at the same time sought to discover the basic reasons why he should advocate the principles of the Reformation. Emotionally, he was committed to them, but he sought to justify his thinking rationally. There was still in his mind, as in that of other nobles a fear of the magical power of the papacy.

On one occasion he earnestly inquired of Martin, "If the pope is the true representative of God and the guardian of the Church, in whose hands are the keys of the kingdom of heaven, must we not, of necessity, be obedient to him? True, we realize that he is a man and, therefore, not perfect; but is he not the representative of The Eternal here upon the earth?"

"I formerly believed that, too," Martin acknowledged, "and for many years I was confident that, although there might be prelates within the Church, bishops, archbishops and cardinals, who could err and fail to interpret God's will for mankind, the pope, in his status as God's representative here on earth, and when he was speaking for God, could not err. But, Sire, I no longer believe that. If the pope can err when speaking as a man, is not his judgment constantly obscured by reason of the fact that man can err?"

"I suppose that would be possible," John acknowledged.

"Not only possible but assuredly so," Martin averred. "You will recall that the kings of England long insisted that they ruled by divine right. As such, whatever they decreed, became, for that very reason, the decree of God. Are you willing to accept their assumption as true?"

"No. Definitely not," John asserted stoutly. "While I believe that a ruler, be he elector or king, should seek to do God's will —as I do—I do not believe that either King Henry of England or Elector John of Saxony are free from ever committing error."

"The same holds true of the pope," Martin insisted. "In fact, history gives evidence of that for some of the popes were notoriously licentious. It would be wonderful if we would have in the world someone who could perfectly interpret the mind of God and of our Lord Jesus Christ, but no such man has ever lived. And Paul, who was truly one of the greatest of the apostles, described himself on one occasion as 'a sinner of which I am chiefest.' If he so regarded himself, could we not assert that the pope also, as a man, must be a sinner, no matter how holy he might be?"

John agreed. This was a sample of one of the many conferences which the two had. John seemed eager to sharpen his thinking on the anvil of Martin's mind. The two frequently disagreed, but their disagreements, as well as the areas in which they thought alike, merely increased the high regard in which each held the other.

In the spring of 1526, the emperor ordered that another diet should be convened, this time at Spires.

"Do you intend to go?" John inquired of Martin. "Undoubtedly you are expected to be present."

"Do you think that I should attend?" Martin asked.

"Decidedly not," the elector replied. "In my judgment you ought not to place yourself in jeopardy again. In any event I shall attend and will represent your interests."

When the diet was convened, the clerical representatives and nobles discovered that, although the emperor had not come, his brother Ferdinand was there to represent him.

Upon his return from the meeting John reported to Martin what had transpired. "Prince Ferdinand opened the meeting with the statement that the emperor had instructed him to say that he was desirous that the Edict of Worms should be immediately enforced. His Majesty was concerned that it had never been put into effect."

"He referred to the edict which insisted that I be put under arrest, did he not?" Martin inquired.

"Precisely, since that was the principal reason for bringing the priests and prelates to Spires along with the various princes who were heads of state," John said.

"So I now place you in jeopardy unless you deliver me to representatives of the emperor or the pope?" Martin asked.

John smiled.

"Not exactly," John replied, "because the diet also decided that in matters of faith the princes were to decide for themselves what form of worship should be adopted in their various provinces. I have decided that the form of worship for Saxony should be *Lutheran.*"

Martin pursed his brow in dismay.

"I wish, Sire, that you would not so designate the form of worship which those of us who have urged reformation upon the Church use. It is not mine at all, but it is the form which I believe Christ Himself would want the Church to adopt. For instance, I am positive that He would not deny the wine, significant of His shed blood which was spilled on Calvary, to the laity, reserving it only for the priests."

John nodded his head.

"And I believe that our Lord would want church services to be held in our own tongue and not in Latin which our people do not understand," Martin continued. "Jesus did not speak to His followers in the Latin tongue or even in the classic Hebrew which was used in temple worship. Instead, our Master spoke to them in their common tongue which was Aramaic."

It is quite possible that John did not understand the points which Martin made, but he believed in Martin and sagely nodded his head.

"Whether or not you desire that our form of worship be called Lutheran, brother Martin," John said, "our people are now thus calling this form of worship to distinguish it from the other."

"That may well be," Martin replied, "but we must never refer to the Church in Saxony as Lutheran. There is one Church only, the Catholic. It is neither Roman, nor German nor English. Instead, it is the Church which our Lord Jesus Christ established."

From the papal viewpoint, the Diet of Spires was as unsatisfactory as previous diets. The German princes were opposed to the attempt to enforce the decision of Worms, and the final vote was to the effect that the decision as to whether or not the decree should be enforced would be postponed until a future diet. A further decision was reached that, in matters of faith, each state should set for its own citizens the form of worship which they should adopt, always remembering that the state was not altogether sovereign and would have to answer to God and the emperor for the type of worship which it adopted. This decision in which the majority of the clergy apparently concurred was not at all one of which the pope could approve.

On the other hand the edict of Worms was declared to be still in effect as far as Luther was concerned but as no means were even suggested by which Martin was to be stopped from preaching or conducting the services of the church according to his own inclinations it was a wholly inconclusive conviction.

As a result Martin was disgusted with the decision.

"It is not an honest one," he told Philip Melancthon. "It is

107

a futile compromise. The princes and the emperor, to save their own faces, have dealt openly in lies. It is laid down that I should be treated according to the ban which was issued at Worms, and that the implications of this ban were to be vigorously enforced.

"Nevertheless, side by side with this decree, is the contradictory one that only at some future diet will it be decided what is good and what is bad in my teaching. I am, at one and the same time, condemned and remanded to a future tribunal. On the other hand the German people are instructed to prosecute me as a criminal and also to wait until I am convicted. The princes must have been either drunk or mad."

"They have been neither, Brother Martin," Philip replied with a smile. "They have merely followed the usual custom of politicians. They have avoided making final decisions. They have found a way by which they apparently make accommodation with the pope and the emperor and yet do not offend the German people."

"H'mph!" Martin grunted. "I would rather they condemned me outright and brought the matter to final issue."

The practical result of the diet's decision was that the princes set about to organize the Church within their own dominions. The majority of the princes favored Martin's concept of the Church and were eager to be free from the domination of Rome. Most of the priests had also espoused the Lutheran cause or, if they were not in accord with it, had left Germany. Among those who had become Lutheran in their thinking was George Spalatin who had been the perfect-general of the Augustinian Hermits. Spalatin had been Martin's warm friend but Martin had not dared to hope that he would follow him into the Reformation movement.

Martin had been so preoccupied with ecclesiastical and political affairs that he failed to realize what had been happening in his own household. It wasn't, therefore, until a friend of Katie's, who had been with her in the convent, bluntly told Martin that he should pay more attention to his wife, that he remembered that he had family duties as well.

Wilhelmina Dorfmann had not left the convent at the time when Katie and the other nuns had escaped, but six months later she and three other nuns had left the convent forever. Like those who had preceded her in leaving the convent, she had come to Wittenberg and had settled there and married a local merchant.

She was a very plain woman, exceedingly outspoken and possessed of a wry variety of humor.

She had come upon Katie in tears one day while Martin was off at a meeting.

"Why the tears, Katie?" she asked, adding facetiously, "Your husband does not beat you?"

"No! No! Never!" Katie protested. "Dr. Luther is always most kind to me."

"Then why are you so unhappy?" Wilhelmina persisted.

"I am not unhappy," Katie avowed through her tears.

"Then you have a strange way of showing happiness," Wilhelmina commented drily.

"Some women do," Katie replied. "But perhaps I am just a wee bit unhappy since I had hoped that Dr. Luther would notice . . ."

"Notice what?"

"That I'm going to have a baby," Katie sobbed. "You would think, wouldn't you, that a man would know when he was about to become a father?"

"You mean that the great Dr. Luther . . ."

"He hasn't said a word to me about it."

"The dolt! The . . . the . . . the . . ." Wilhelmina sputtered. "I shall most certainly inform the blind doctor."

"You must not," Katie protested.

"Someone had better tell him," Wilhelmina insisted.

"He will soon find out," Katie said.

"When the child is born," Wilhelmina said derisively.

Wilhelmina stayed for lunch with the Luthers that noon. Katie glanced at her apprehensively but Wilhelmina had evidently decided that she would let Katie tell Martin in her own way. When Katie was apparently completely reassured, however, Wilhelmina with subtle guile inquired of the reformer, "Are you hoping, Dr. Luther, that your child will be a boy, or would you prefer that the infant will be a girl?"

Startled, Martin exclaimed, "What?"

"A boy or a girl?" Wilhelmina persisted.

"A boy or a . . . what?" Martin exploded.

"Yes," Wilhelmina returned, adding, "Fathers usually hope that their firstborn will be sons."

Startled, Martin looked to Katie for an explanation. Katie flushed, looking down at her plate without comment.

"Praise God!" Martin ejaculated.

He left his place at the table and put his arms around Katie. "My beloved!" he whispered. "My dear wife. How could I have been so blind?"

Wilhelmina smiled triumphantly.

11

A son was born to the former monk and nun in Wittenberg. Martin was in his forties, Katie sixteen years younger. Martin felt embarrassed at the idea of being a father for the first time at an age when some men were becoming grandfathers, and there was still a sense of impropriety in having begotten a son when, for so many years, he had been conditioned to accept celibacy as his way of life. But, even though he was awkward in the manner in which he took his little son into his arms, Martin enjoyed the experience of fatherhood.

This boy was his, bone of his bone, flesh of his flesh; and he felt a great pride in the part which he had played in bringing into the world this chubby bit of humanity. Especially delighted was he when visitors gravely commented on the fact that he very much resembled Martin.

"But no," he would disclaim. "He is the image of his beautiful mother."

"Not so. He has his father's strong chin," Katie insisted over and over again.

"He does look a determined lad," Martin acknowledged proudly.

"And he shouts like Dr. Luther when he wants his food," Katie said.

One of those who commented on the child's appearance, quite naturally, was Philip Melancthon.

When Katie made her customary observation concerning the likeness of father and son in the matter of eating and shouting, Philip remarked with a smile, "He is blessed with a good stomach and strong lungs."

Martin, who seemed always to be present when his son was being exhibited, demanded, "Who has strong lungs, the boy or I?"

"Both of you," Philip replied.

Before Katie was up and about after their son's birth, Martin and she discussed the name which should be given to their first-born.

"He should be called Martin for his father," Katie insisted. "He deserves to have your name."

"No. No," Martin objected. "He should not be burdened all of his life by being compared to me. If he should do something wrong, people would say, 'What can you expect of him? He is just like his father.' That, at least, would be said by those who have opposed me. And if he did not seem to measure up to the few virtues which I may possess, my friends would shake their heads and lament because he had failed me. With a name of his own, he could make a way for himself in the world."

"Well, then, what name do you suggest?" Katie demanded.

"Hans is a good name," Martin announced. "That is my father's name. It is also the name of your father. And it is the name of our good friend, Dr. Johannes Bugenhagen."

Dr. Bugenhagen had become the minister of the parish church in Wittenberg. There were those who had insisted that Martin should take this assignment, and it had been his for a short time after the church had broken with Rome, but Martin had pointed out that he could not be a good pastor when he had so many other responsibilities. As it was, he preached as often in the church as did Dr. Bugenhagen, but the latter became the official pastor of the church.

"And who will baptize our little Hans?" Katie inquired of Martin one day.

"I should like to have Philip officiate," Martin replied, "because he has been like a brother to me, but I don't know whether he would really know how to do it. He has probably never baptized a babe before. No, Dr. Bugenhagen should be the one to serve. Philip could assist him, of course, and offer the prayer."

So it was arranged, and the first Sunday after Katie was able to leave their home, the baptism was celebrated in the parish Church. Martin was a proud father as he presented his firstborn to the minister for baptism in the name of the Father, Son and Holy Ghost. The service was a familiar one at which Martin had

112

officiated many times, but the words were spoken in German instead of Latin which Martin had used when he had been a monk.

This important event over, Martin plunged with greater zeal than ever into his work in the university and his writing.

One morning, shortly before Christmas, his thoughts turned from theology to the little household over which he presided, and from that household to the one which centuries before had been set up in a temporary shelter, a stable in Bethlehem. It had been a long time since Martin had composed a hymn, but there flashed into his mind the words of a song which, it seemed to him, demanded to be written.

Eagerly he set down phrases and sentences on paper, then crossed out some, rewrote the poem once and then again, at the same time humming a tune. Finally, after much contemplating, he arrived at a phraseology which he approved, penning the words of a lullaby which, forever thereafter, would be known as his "cradle hymn":

> Ah, dearest Jesus, holy Child,
>   Make Thee a bed, soft, undefiled
> Within my heart, that it may be
>   A quiet chamber kept for Thee.
>
> My heart for very joy doth leap,
>   My lips no more can silence keep;
> I, too, must sing with joyful tongue,
>   That sweetest ancient cradle song.
>
> Glory to God in highest heaven,
>   Who unto man His Son hath given,
> While angels sing with tender mirth,
>   A glad new year to all the earth.

Katie was at work in the kitchen when Martin finished the hymn. He hurried from his study into the kitchen, shouting as he trotted down the corridor, "I have it. I have it."

"And, pray, what earth-shaking idea do you have now?" Katie inquired.

"A beautiful lullaby to sing to my little Hans," he announced.

"And for that you interrupt the important work of meal preparation?" Katie retorted severely. "A woman is busy preparing meals, keeping a huge house clean, and with only one little servant girl to help her, and you spend your time writing lullabies!"

"But this is a Christmas lullaby and we'll ask Dr. Bugenhagen to have it sung for the Christmas services," he said.

"Very well. Go and see the good doctor but leave me to my work," Katie replied.

"But I want you to be the first to hear it," Martin insisted. "Come into his bedroom and listen."

Little Hans was cooing in his crib as the two tip-toed in.

"See!" exclaimed Martin, "He's awake. You want me to sing to you, do you, little Hans?"

He turned to Katie. "See," he said, "he nods his head. He is a discriminating little beggar. He wants his father to sing this new cradle song to him."

Martin picked up Hans with tender solicitude and cradled the babe in his arms. Softly he began to sing. As Martin crooned the melody, Hans joined his father with cooing baby sounds. Then, as Martin began the second stanza, Hans' lower lip turned down and he began to sob. Before Martin had finished his song Hans' sobs became a lusty howl.

"Very discriminating, your son," Katie remarked. "Here! Let me take him."

She gathered the babe into her arms and felt of the child's undergarments. She began to laugh.

"It wasn't your singing that troubled him," she observed to her husband. "It's just that the little one . . . well, he is wet."

"That happens," Martin commented drily. "Very well, *Hanschen,* I shall sing it over to you again at a more appropriate time. Meanwhile I shall take this over to Dr. Bugenhagen. He may want to have it sung for the Christmas service."

Martin was right. The song was sung at every service in the church on the Sunday preceding Christmas and again on Christmas Day. Dr. Bugenhagen asked Martin to sing the entire song from beginning to end for the Christmas congregation, and then had the congregation sing in unison.

"Sing it quietly, dear friends," Martin suggested. "It is a lullaby — not a great oratorio."

Later he remarked to Katie, "As I sang, I imagined that I was back again in my student days and that the congregation thought of me, as my fellow students did years ago, as 'Musicus.'"

"It was lovely, Martin dear," Katie said.

Martin's heart rejoiced. Katie now called him Martin instead of Dr. Luther when she was in her most tender mood. While it was right and proper, according to the custom of the time, for her to refer to her husband as the "*Herr Doktor*" when speaking to others, he longed to have her feel an intimacy with him in the precincts of their own home which had nothing to do with his rank in the ecclesiastical or educational world.

Since Martin and Katie had taken care of the matter of baptizing their child and had registered his birth in the parish church, Martin turned to other matters. In a conference which he held with Pastor Bugenhagen and Philip Melancthon he asked them what they considered to be among the principal needs of what was an evolving Evangelical Church.

"One great difficulty which we face," Johannes Bugenhagen stated, "is the lack of a book which we could use in our services. Before we broke with Rome we had the missal for the use of both priests and people. We have prepared nothing with which to replace it. Too, many of our ministers, having never become accustomed to preaching, do not know what to say to their congregations."

"We need a book of worship then," Martin suggested.

"Yes, and a hymn book as well. You have written several hymns yourself," Philip remarked. "Would it be possible to have such a book published and distributed to the congregation? You could include many of the hymns with which the people are familiar and which were written before ever there was a Roman church."

"I think it could be done," Martin assured him.

"And we need a catechism for our children," Philip, the theologically-minded teacher, reminded Martin. "We should indoctrinate them now in their formative years so that when they grow older they will have strong convictions concerning their faith."

"A catechism then," Martin noted, jotting down this item on a piece of foolscap.

"But our older people are as ignorant of the basis of our faith as are the children," Dr. Bugenhagen said decisively. "There should be a succinct statement of our faith for them as well."

"Another catechism?" Martin inquired.

"Well, why not?" Dr. Bugenhagen returned. "Could you not prepare a short, elementary catechism for our children and a longer version for adults? Perhaps even the longer version should be written in the most elementary terms, however, since our people, except for learned doctors and university professors, would not understand a statement of our faith unless it was written in very simple language."

Martin told the elector about these suggestions.

"If you will prepare these books I will arrange for their publication," the elector promised him, "and will give to each church in Saxony a supply for its own use. Perhaps some of the other princes will be willing to do the same for their provinces."

With this assurance, Martin first prepared a booklet containing twenty-four hymns, eighteen of which he wrote himself. He not only wrote the words but also composed the music for many of them. He next set for himself the task of preparing a catechism for children, later to be known as "The Smaller Catechism." The catechism consisted of questions and answers which set forth in succinct form the dogmas of the Reformation faith.

The catechetical method of teaching was not new to students for it was used even in the universities in addition to lectures. It was as much a part of elementary education as spelling lessons or the copy-book method of learning to write. It was expected that children would become letter perfect in memorizing both questions and answers.

"Should not the questions be explained to them first — and the answers as well?" Philip Melancthon asked.

" 'Twould be well to do so," Martin conceded, "but I am not greatly concerned that they should be. I am more desirous that they learn both from memory and store them in their minds. Later, as they grow older, what they have learned by rote in childhood will become clear to them."

"True," Philip conceded.

The Smaller Catechism was published and, as the elector had promised, it was distributed to all the schools in Saxony. This made their use area-wide since the schools were all under the supervision of the local churches. While some of the ministers did not altogether approve of all Luther's views, they had no intention of challenging the elector. Other provinces also began to use the pamphlet.

Before launching out upon the writing of the Larger Catechism, such as his two friends had suggested, Martin wrote a number of sermons and arranged for their publication, sermons couched in such simple language that even the humblest peasant could be expected to understand them. These were published and sent out to the pastors of all the churches in Saxony. Accompanying the booklet was the notation, "These may be used by my brother ministers, if desired, especially by those of you who are so busy with your many labors that you may not have time for sermon preparation."

"I hope that they will not lean upon them as crutches," Martin remarked to Philip.

"Some of them undoubtedly will," Philip replied shrugging his shoulders.

His minor writing tasks completed, Martin began his work on the Longer Catechism which was to be used by adults. He had just begun this important work when his labors were interrupted by the advent of a widespread siege of illness. The plague — probably a virus disease — struck Germany in the winter of 1527 and ran rampant. People died by the thousands. Sometimes whole villages were decimated.

Neither Martin nor his wife were stricken, but little Hans was. His fever mounted in one day until his tiny body seemed to be burning up with it. He was a robust child, but he speedily wasted away until his body appeared to be nothing but bones, sparsely covered by parchment. His chubby, rosy cheeks paled and then aternately seemed to be afire. He took on the appearance of a miniature old man, weak, emaciated.

Wittenberg seemed to be hit harder than any other community in all of Germany. The university people fled to Jena and set up their colleges there. The faculty accompanied the students with the exception of Philip and Martin who stayed on in Wittenberg.

"You had best go with the others, Philip," Martin urged. "You can do nothing here."

"I could not desert you," Philip replied. "I must stay with you, and Katie, and little Hans." Noting that Martin was about to object, he hastily added, "Nor do I think only of you and your family. I feel that it is my responsibility to remain with this stricken city to render what help I can."

"But there is nothing that you can do, dear friend," Martin objected.

"I can at least tend fires, make soup for the stricken families, and bury the dead if that is needed," Philip insisted. "No. I shall stay here; and the university people will eventually return also when the plague has run its course."

Philip moved into the Luther parsonage so that he might be near at hand if calls came for service. Martin walked the floor day and night, occasionally lying down for a few moments when he was completely exhausted. He did many of the chores about the house for Katie kept to the sick-room constantly, wiping the face and chest of her baby with cool, wet cloths, feeding him broth to keep up his strength.

After two weeks Han's fever broke. When Katie told Martin that there had been a turn for the better her husband murmured, "*Gott sei dank*. God be thanked!"

Eventually the plague seemed to finish its course and Wittenberg began to plan to resume normal activity. But there were few homes which had not been visited by the angel of death; and now older people, and men, women, and children whose vitality had been sapped by sickness began to drop off. The ranks of the elderly folk were decimated and many tiny babies were also taken Little Hans was one of the few who were spared.

The experience through which Martin had passed, had something to do with mellowing his character. He also became more introspective, less impulsive. Certainly the anxious vigils which he had observed had given him time to ponder upon the mysteries of life and death as never before in his life. He continued to call upon those who had lost loved ones to comfort them; and he also visited those who were ill or weakened by the long run which the plague had had.

"It is the least that I can do for these good people," he explained to Katie. "We were so near to losing our precious little son that I think I can understand better what those parents went through who lost one or more of their children."

Martin discovered that some of these people were in dire straits. They lacked food and clothing. They didn't have sufficient money to buy either coal or wood for their fireplaces. Consequently, although the plague had run its course, many were still dying.

"I am going out to beg for funds and clothing," Martin told Katie. "This is a time when people must share with one another, and I have had excellent training in this, as you know. When I was a student at the university I sang for my meals, and then, when I entered the priesthood, I often went out of the monastery to beg money for its support."

"But, Martin, you have never begged since that time."

"No, I haven't, but it will be good for my soul to invite people to give for such a good cause."

118

As soon as Philip learned about Martin's plans he insisted on joining him.

"If you will sing as you did in Erfurt I can hold the collection basket," he said.

There were few people on the streets of Wittenberg those bitter, cold days, but many people opened their doors or windows and hastily deposited silver or copper coins in the baskets which Philip presented to them. With the proceeds, Martin and Philip bought meat and vegetables for soup.

"Nourishing soup is the best remedy for their weakness when people are recovering from the plague," Martin noted. "Hot soup and warm bedrooms are what these poor people need."

Philip continued to spend his nights in the parsonage with Martin and Katie so that he would be readily accessible in the event that there were calls for their services. Either Martin or Philip went daily to the cemetery after the carts had collected those who had died the preceding day.

"We had better conduct services over the remains of those who died during the height of the plague, too," Martin suggested to Philip. "No one should be interred in the ground save as words from Holy Scripture are read over their remains and prayers offered," Martin said.

With the advent of spring and a break in the weather, deaths which were due to the plague or to complications which developed as a result of the sickness, finally diminished. The university authorities and the students moved back to Wittenberg and the city became alive again. A few students had died in Jena, and other parts of the country had also been stricken, but Wittenberg had been harder hit than other areas.

Martin resumed his teaching in the university and he also preached frequently in the parish church. In a way, it became a period of calm for Martin. He worked hard on his expositions of the Scriptures. His Biblical hero was Paul. Again and again in his writings he made reference to the Pauline doctrine of justification by faith which Martin regarded as the very cornerstone of the Christian religion.

On one occasion, after spending some time with the pastoral epistle of James, confronted by James' statement, "Show me thy faith without thy works and I will show thee my faith by my works." To be sure, he failed to understand James' point of view that genuine faith would result in works and that the works to which

James referred was not the "good works" advocated by the Catholic Church but referred, instead, to lives which were dedicated to the service of Almighty God, that they did not refer to an attempt to win the favor of God by performing certain good deeds but were the basis of a way of life which was born out of faith.

Late in 1527, a second child was born to Katie and Martin whom they named Elizabeth.

"She is a Christmas present to her lovely mother," Martin remarked as he viewed the child in her mother's arms. From the very beginning, however, Elizabeth was a sickly child and died the following summer.

As Martin and Katie stood beside the little grave in the parish cemetery Katie murmured, "God has punished me for my many sins."

"No, no, dear heart," Martin objected. "Our Father is a loving God. You are a sinner, surely, as are we all and I more than others, but God would not take the life of our little Elizabeth to punish us for our sins. His beloved Son indicated how He felt toward the little ones when He said, 'Suffer the little children and forbid them not to come unto me, for of such is the kingdom of heaven.' Our little one has entered into the Kingdom which we, too, shall hope to enter some day. Be assured of that."

"She has not gone into limbo?" Katie asked, tears coursing down her cheeks.

"There is no such place as limbo," Martin assured her. "Nowhere in the Scriptures do we find any reference to such a place. It is a pagan superstition which was born out of ancient Grecian and Roman beliefs. It has no part whatsoever in the Christian faith."

With that assurance Katie seemed content. She was a calm and contemplative person. If Martin were, as he described himself, a firebrand, she was a calm pool of water which could quench the fires which he started. She had no intention of quenching his ardor for reformation, but when the fires occasionally got out of hand on those occasions when Martin and his friends became especially ardent in their zeal for their special doctrine and sometimes so vehement that they seemed to be divided in their thinking, she would diplomatically guide them to friendly compromise.

Philip Melancthon's temperament was similar to Katie's and he also helped Martin to avoid pitfalls which might have split the Reformation group in Germany.

There were plenty of trials to test a man's temper in those days. Rumors had been rife that either the emperor or the pope intended to raise armies to send into Germany to put down the Reformation. So authentic did these rumors seem to be, that the Elector John of Saxony and Prince Philip of Hesse actually began to conscript men for troops to defend their provinces.

Actually there was no basis whatsoever for the rumor. There had been difficulties between the crown and the papacy which had led, in 1627, to the sacking of Rome by Bourbon, Catholic prince of Spain. He claimed to be acting under authority of the emperor although it is doubtful if the emperor had approved. In any event these difficulties effectively precluded action against Germany on the part of either the papacy or the empire.

12

THE difficulties between the pope and empire had been finally, if only temporarily, resolved before the spring of 1529. Both pope and emperor began, therefore, to pay attention once more to "that mad monk" as they had termed Luther. They made what, for them, was an astonishing discovery that, far from suffering a waning support in Germany, Martin had actually been enjoying greater popularity and had built up a larger personal constituency than he had had before.

Nor had Martin been intimidated into recanting from the positions which he had previously held. Instead, he had become more decided and positive in his beliefs, firmly convinced that he was battling on God's side for the right. He equated the pope and his advisors with "devils." He became increasingly aware of the other groups which were striving for reformation: Zwingli at Basel; Calvin in Geneva; Erasmus, with whom, while the latter was still at Oxford and Cambridge, he had had many disagreements. What had formerly been slight breezes of reformation had finally become a mighty rushing wind.

Both the pope and the emperor became greatly concerned and, in 1529, another blow was struck against the Reformation when the proscriptive decree of the 1521 diet was again revived. Now that Charles had made his peace with the pope, it seemed a propitious time to the latter to assert once more the thesis that the pontiff was supreme with the intention, basically, of securing from the emperor and all of the princes, the recognition of the spiritual authority of the papacy.

However, the Reformation had made such headway throughout Germany, that the princes were quite unwilling to declare themselves for the pope. Instead, therefore, of expressing a readiness to enforce the decree of 1521, they drew up a document which, in the realm of religion, was the equivalent of the Magna Carta and the Bill of Rights in the field of political liberty. It was entitled, "Liberation of the Human Mind from the Dominion of Error, and its Consecration to the Ackowleged Supremacy of Divine Truth." The princes termed it a "protest," and from this word came the designation, "Protestant," by which the advocates of ecclesiastical reform became known thereafter.

The Elector John showed a copy of the protest to Martin. When Luther observed the list of names which had been affixed to the document — John of Saxony; Ernest and Francis, dukes of Brunswick-Lunenberg; Wolfgang, of Anhalt; George, the margrave of Hesse-Homberg — he said, "Truly, Sire, these good men have now openly declared themselves. How greatly your esteemed father would have rejoiced if he had lived to see the day when men of their worth would declare themselves as on the side of reform."

However, another movement sprang up at almost the same time, one which Martin did not approve but one which sprang naturally out of the other protest. The peasants, whose battle for freedom had been put down by the princes, decided to publish a series of demands themselves and post them in every market-place in Germany. Copies of their document were sent to all of the princes and also to Martin Luther.

Their protest read as follows: "It has been custom hitherto for men to hold others as their own property, which is most pitiable considering that Christ has delivered and redeemed us all, the lowly as well as the great, by the shedding of His precious blood. Accordingly, it is consistent with Scripture that we should be free and should wish to be so. We, therefore, take it for granted that you will release us from serfdom as true Christians, unless it should be shown from the Gospel that we should be serfs."

The peasants, greatly embarrassing Luther, had put him on the horns of a dilemma which he himself had created. Martin's father had often expressed himself as opposed to the exploitation of miners by the mine owners, until he had finally become an employer of labor himself as the proprietor of a foundry and smelter. In his younger manhood, too, Martin would have agreed with the peasants, but he owed so much in the way of support to princes such as Philip of Hesse and John of Saxony that he could not declare himself as a proponent of the peasants' point of view.

Instead, Martin issued a statement in which he declared that "This article would make all men equal and so change the spiritual Kingdom of Christ into an external worldly one. Impossible! An earthly kingdom cannot exist without inequality of persons. Some must be free, others serfs, some rulers, others subjects. As St. Paul said, 'In Christ there is neither bond nor free.'"

Martin had insisted that every person should be free to interpret the Scriptures in the light of his own reason and conscience, but he had gradually come to believe that if this principle were put into effect, there would be so many strange interpretations of the Scriptures, that he began to hedge. Instead of permitting the private interpretation of the Scriptures, he came to believe that there should be some kind of uniformity in deciding what was the true meaning of any disputed portions of Holy Writ, and that the best way to insure this end was to make the temporal rulers responsible for the beliefs of their subjects.

He disagreed with both Calvin and Zwingli and was impatient with them when they could not accept his interpretations of various portions of the Bible, although he acknowledged their right to disagree with him. On the other hand, his disagreement with Erasmus, who had once commanded Martin's highest respect, led him to pronounce strong diatribes against the noted scholar. Erasmus had left the priesthood but had sought to remain within the Church. By this time Martin had come to believe that no true Christian could remain within the Roman Church although he contended that he and his followers were true members of *"The* Church."

During Martin's years in Wittenberg he noted that there were many young men, some priests and others university scholars, who were seeking the light. After the fashion of many continental and English scholars, many of them wandered from Geneva, where for a time they sat at the feet of Calvin, to Basel, where both Zwingli and Erasmus attracted some truth-seeking scholars, to Wittenberg to listen to lectures by Luther. Still others made their way to England to attend the universities there, since many members of the clergy as well as university professors had also broken with Rome.

In 1529, hoping to unite the Protestant forces, Luther and Zwingli arranged for a conference in which they would attempt to reconcile their differences and draw up a statement of common belief. Zwingli's religious views were much broader than Luther's.

124

He was not as insistent as was Martin that other Protestants should believe exactly as he did.

One reason for Zwingli's more tolerant attitude to others, in all probability, was that he had not faced as much opposition as Martin had. He had grown up in a Swiss canton where, as in other cantons of that small country, there had always been a passionate love of liberty and short shrift for any kind of authoritarianism. This had been the spirit which had attracted Calvin to French-speaking Geneva.

Luther and Zwingli were aware of the differences which separated them, especially their disagreement concerning the nature of the sacrament of the Lord's Supper. While, therefore, they talked about holding a conference, they actually kept postponing the event. But Prince Philip of Hesse, who was always impatient of procrastination, felt that they should meet immediately and attempt to find a common ground for union. He was one who believed that theologians should put their faith to work instead of keeping it in the realm of classroom discussion.

He, therefore, pressed Martin for a decision, saying that he would invite the conferees. Martin responded bluntly to the invitation which he received, saying, "Your grace can easily see that all conference will be in vain if both sides come with the determination to give up nothing. All I have seen hitherto leads me to think that they will stand by their position even after they have rightly understood our reasons; as I know well, I cannot yield when I have heard theirs; and I am certain that they are wrong."

The issue, of course, was the different positions which the two men maintained concerning the nature of the sacrament of the Lord's Supper. Zwingli believed that both bread and water remained such during and before the time when believers partook of the elements. Luther did not believe, as did the Roman Catholics, that bread and wine actually changed into the body and blood of Christ when they were blessed by the priest so that a communicant actually partook again of the body and blood of the Master, but he did believe that, in the act of eating the bread and drinking the wine which remained just physical elements, one still did partake spiritually of the actual body and blood of the Saviour. They were agreed that both ministers and people should partake of both bread and wine. The Roman Catholic position was that the wine was reserved exclusively for the priests.

There were other issues also which divided them. Some of them were matters of emphasis as, for instance, the doctrine of predestination. While Zwingli accepted the doctrine, as did both Luther and Calvin, it did not make such a strong appeal to him as it did to his two contemporaries. Nor did Zwingli shut the door of fellowship in the face of those who did not share his creed as readily as Martin did.

Ulrich Zwingli also insisted that God had more channels of grace than one only and that He did not condemn many to perdition because of original sin. He went further still and insisted that heaven was not only open to all believers but it was open as well to the great moral teachers whose deeds and teachings had uplifted humanity. He referred particularly to the philosophers whose teachings antedated Christianity.

Zwingli cited Socrates as an example. Luther could not agree with such a tolerant point of view. He believed that a man was justified by faith and, since Socrates lived long before Christ did, his doom was sealed.

At six in the morning on October 2, 1529, the confrontation between Luther and Zwingli took place in the banquet hall of Philip of Hesse's castle in Marburg. A long table, covered with a velvet runner, was set in the center of the hall.

Before the proceedings began Martin chalked the words, "This is my body," on the cloth directly in front of his seat. When Prince Philip signaled for the parley to commence Martin immediately began the discussion.

The disputants argued heatedly for hours. Both Martin and Zwingli had proponents for their causes to speak for their points of view. The meeting became more and more animated as time went on: neither side would yield an inch to the other. They spoke also in order to win the approval of the considerable number of interested spectators who were present. The meeting finally broke up for dinner when, for a brief period of time, the disputants forgot their argument and had a period when they set aside their differences and dined in friendly fashion.

After dinner, however, the two groups began where they had left off. Zwingli presented his views on the sacrament of the Lord's Supper once more, ending with his summary in which he said:

"Christ's words, 'This is my body; this is my blood,' were figurative just as were the words, 'I am the door,' and 'I am the true vine,' which Jesus used on other occasions. Just as Christ

126

is in heaven manifestly His Body is also there. A body must occupy space, and it cannot be in two places at once. When Christ was here on earth His body was here and not in heaven."

Martin listened impatiently. When Zwingli had finished Martin replied, "Dr. Zwingli, you have placed impossible limitations upon the power of the Almighty. God is above mathematics. Christ's body is in the sacrament as the sword is in the scabbard."

The two viewpoints were so far apart that, although the argument continued through the day and the day which followed, the two could arrive at no common ground of understanding. They did agree on eleven of twelve articles of faith which Martin had drawn up but could not agree on the last which had to do with the sacrament of the Lord's Supper. Zwingli, Luther, Melancthon, and Zwingli's friend Ecolampadius appended their signatures to the eleven articles on which they were in agreement but did not sign the twelfth.

Zwingli, deeply moved by the occasion, burst into tears. He held out his hand to Martin to indicate the fact that they were really in close agreement on the essentials of Christian faith but Martin refused to accept the proffered hand.

Sadly Zwingli remarked to Luther, "You have another spirit."

Despite the lack of cordiality, Zwingli spent one more day with Martin. Martin sought to make amends for his failure to extend the hand of fellowship and they passed the day in friendly discourse, eschewing a discussion of theological issues. When they parted, each thought that the other had finally agreed with him.

Shortly afterward Martin announced to the elector, "We left Marburg with the hope that as the other side had conceded all the Christian articles and had receded from its former error concerning the Holy Sacrament they would in time completely unite with us."

Zwingli returned to Basel and announced that his group had won at Marburg. When Martin heard from friends that Zwingli claimed that Martin had receded from his position, he was deeply disgusted. He had become so accustomed to winning disputes, that he was unwilling to brook opposition from any source.

To be sure, Martin had been so despondent for some time following the death of his daughter Elizabeth in August, 1528, that for months he had not been his usually ebullient self. Elizabeth

127

had lived for only eight months and Martin had felt crushed when she passed away. This was one of the causes of his shortness of temper. Another daughter was to be born to Martin and Katie on May 4th, 1529, and for this Martin would thank God. Still he never seemed to get over the death of Elizabeth.

Actually, although Martin loved children, he was over forty before he had to assume the role of father, and he was not well equipped to take over the responsibilities of parenthood. Crying babies made him nervous and when he was embroiled in controversy, he was inclined to take out his irritations upon those who disagreed with him.

Later he would feel sorry for having permitted his temper to get away with him, but he was not so constituted that he could easily sue for forgiveness from those whom he had offended. Only Philip Melancthon could put up with his outbursts without rancor, recognizing the greatness of Martin's heart and the courage which was basic to his nature.

While Martin had been conferring with Zwingli and his friends about a possible union, the princes were appearing before the emperor. Before they set forth on their journey, they were joined by representatives of several of the free towns, including Strasburg, Ulm and Nuremberg. The city councils of those cities had declared their firm adherence to the principles which the princes had announced.

However, by the time that the delegations reached him, the emperor had made his peace with the pope. Among other promises which he made to the Bishop of Rome was one that he would win back for Rome the estranged allegiance of the German people, even if force should be necessary to accomplish this end. When the princes and their deputies appeared before him at Placenza he received them gruffly and informed them that he had no intention of acceding to their requests. Instead, he indicated, he intended to force them to give their allegiance to the pope, however extreme the methods of accomplishing that end might be.

Furthermore, he denounced the princes for appealing to him instead of to the pope. He ordered that all who had signed such a petition should be confined in prison for their presumption in appealing to him over the head of the pope. That this decision was made for political reasons seemed evident when he did not actually take them into custody. The decision of the emperor accomplished one thing, however; it assured the pope of Charles' apparently firm intention to be a loyal son of Rome.

This proved to be a very shrewd move on the part of Charles, for within a month he was summoned to Rome for his very solemn inauguration to the throne of the Caesars. This should have occurred several years earlier and would have taken place then, had it not been for the controversy between pope and emperor, a controversy which had finally been resolved.

Cordial relations between the two having been re-established, Charles also urged upon the pope the wisdom of convening another church council. He felt that if the pope would elect to undertake some of the reforms which the German clergy had been demanding, they could be won back to the papacy and the German princes would give greater loyalty to the empire. The pope cannily avoided the issue by pointing out the new development in the east, where the Turks, under their victorious sultan, Solyman, were again threatening the frontier.

"This is no time to hold a council," the pope informed him. "We must wait for peaceful times."

The pope was also fearful of new losses to the Protestants. When the Turks captured Hungary, Archduke Ferdinand, seeking to win the aid of the German princes in recapturing his kingdom from the invaders, began to advocate tolerance for the adherents of Luther who had settled in his realm.

The entire empire seemed to be on the point of disintegration. For this reason, the emperor believed that a council might help to keep it intact, but the pope believed that if the empire could be kept in turmoil, Charles would be more dependent upon the papacy and more amenable to the pope's direction. The pope was undoubtedly fearful that if the empire was at peace, the emperor might make an attempt to institute some of the reforms which the German princes advocated.

The fires everywhere were still being kindled which were fed by the unwillingness of the papacy to admit to any error. In Bavaria, a priest named Leonard Cesar, had been burnt alive because he had espoused Evangelical doctrine. He was just one of many who were martyred.

After Leonard's martyrdom, Martin wrote a letter to a friend in which he said:

O miserable Luther, so unlike Leonard! I, a verbose preacher of the Word; he a mighty doer of it. O that I were prepared, I will not say with double, but even half his spirit, to conquer Satan and surrender my life! Blessed be God, who, among so many ministers, has shown to us at least one glorious spectacle of His grace, unworthy as we are.

Pray for me, my brother Michael, that Christ may enable me to imitate our Leonard. Not only king, but Cesar, he was deservedly called; because he conquered him to whose power there is no equal here on earth. He was not only *priest*, yea, and true *pope*, in that his own body he presented as a living and holy sacrifice, acceptable to God. And very rightly was he called *Leonhard*, that is *strength of a lion*; for so was he, bold and undaunted.

The note of self-deprecation manifested in the letter was one of Martin's characteristics. He always felt that he lacked in courage what others possessed. Yet he would have been willing to yield up his life for the truth as he saw it. The fact that he did not need to suffer martyrdom seemed to make him regard himself as less in his devotion to God than those who had given up their lives.

In the Netherlands also, the fires of persecution had begun to burn brightly. The emperor was not inhibited there, as in Germany, in his persecution of the Lutherans. In fact, the only area in his domain in which he trod lightly was in the German states for the princes were almost unanimously back of Luther.

13

*L*ATE in 1529, Charles V. decided that he would make a final trial to reach a settlement of the religious question. Adrian VI was dead and had been succeeded by Clement VII. Charles had no love for the new pope in view of the fact that in 1527 the latter had conspired with Francis I of France to form a "Holy League" against Charles. Charles had quickly nipped the conspiracy in the bud and had actually imprisoned the pope for six months, but he had never forgiven the pope for plotting against him.

However, Charles regarded himself as a loyal Catholic and, if he could keep the pope in line and ready to endorse his programs and policies, he was willing to accord the Roman pontiff at least nominal leadership of the religious forces of the empire.

Charles decided that he would call another diet in order to try to find a settlement for the ecclesiastical differences between the Protestant and Catholic forces once and for all. Charles recognized, if the pope would not, the fact that the empire was actually divided into two segments. The Germans were now thoroughly Protestant with the exception of a few centers, notably Bavaria, where the clergy still proclaimed their allegiance to Rome and followed the Roman pattern of worship.

The emperor felt that if he could crush the Protestant movement, he would thereby unify the empire. He had defeated King Francis at the battle of Pavia in 1525, and France had thereby become a tributary nation if not actually a part of the empire. If, therefore, he could bring Germany back into the Roman Catholic fold, he would, in truth, be the undisputed emperor of the Holy Roman Empire.

He had scheduled the diet for April, 1530. He had selected

131

Augsburg as the meeting place, but he had taken such a leisurely journey to that center, apparently to show his contempt for the princes and clerics whom he had summoned to meet there, that he did not arrive until the fifteenth of June. He entered the city like a conquering Caesar, his brother Ferdinand riding on one side of his carriage of state, and Cardinal Campeggio, representative of the pope, on the other.

On June 16th he celebrated the great Catholic festival of the Feast of Corpus Christi. The Elector of Saxony also took part in the procession which inaugurated the festival, although his Protestant sympathies were well-known. He rode beside the emperor and carried the Sword of State. He did not divulge even to his closest friends his reason for so doing, but it was probably his intention by this action to indicate that he was loyal to the emperor although denying allegiance to the pope. The Archbishop of Mainz carried the host at the head of the procession.

There was no intention on this occasion of allowing Martin to participate in the deliberations of the diet, for fear he would dominate the meeting by his eloquent powers of speech and his clear, succinct arguments which were based upon his interpretations of Biblical teaching. Instead, Philip Melancthon had been delegated to represent the Protestant forces, a choice which Martin warmly approved.

Instead of going to Augsburg, Martin was persuaded by the Elector of Saxony to repair to the castle of Coburg, an impregnable fortress located on the borders of Thuringia. The elector was fearful that the emperor would take advantage of the convening of the diet to arrest Martin. The castle was built high on a hill above the city which surrounded it. Martin occupied the principal part of the structure which was called the Prince's Tower. With Martin were two companion secretaries, one his nephew, Viet Dietrich, and the other a former student of his at Wittenberg. In addition, the elector assigned to him a retinue of thirty men.

Before Philip set out for Augsburg, he received a letter from Martin. The latter wrote:

> I have at length arrived at my Sinai, dear Philip: but of this Sinai I will make a Sion: I will raise thereon three tabernacles, one to the Psalmist, another to the Prophets and lastly one to Aesop. There is nothing here to prevent my solitude from being complete. I reside in a vast abode which overlooks the castle. I have the keys of all of its apartments. There are scarcely thirty persons present

within the fortress. They are actually here to guard me. Twelve of them are watchers by night, and two others are sentinels by day. They are constantly posted on the castle height.

For some considerable time Martin could find comparatively little to occupy his time. He spent a few hours in his study daily, partly in continuing to work on his expositions of the Scriptures, partly in writing to his family, since he was exceedingly lonely and eager for a glimpse of his wife and children.

Fancifully he called his retreat, "The Realm Of The Birds." In one of his letters to Katie he wrote:

> There is a grove just under our window like a small forest. And there, strangely enough, the jackdaws and crows are holding a diet. They fly in and out of this grove, and keep up a racket day and night without ceasing, as if they were all drunk. Young and old chatter in such a fashion and with so much earnestness, that I wonder they have any voice left at the close of their meetings. I should like to know whether there are any knights and warriors left in Wittenberg. It seems as if the representatives who are here must have gathered from all over the world. I have not yet seen their emperor; but the nobility and gentry constantly flit about before our eyes. They are not extravagantly clothed but are all attired in one color, and all alike gray-eyed. And they all sing the same song, a psalm of praise to Almighty God.
>
> They care nothing for palaces. Their hall is vaulted with the broad expanse of heaven, and its walls are as wide as the world. They do not ask for horses or armor. They are all equipped with feathered chariots with which to escape the hunters. They are high and mighty lords, but I don't know yet what they are debating. So far as I have been able to understand, they plan a great war against wheat, barley, oats, malt and all sorts of grain. Many a one will show himself a hero and do brave deeds.

Soon after the date which had been originally set for the diet to be convened but before the emperor arrived officially to open the convocation, a paper was presented by the town councils, of Reutlingen and Nuremberg, two free cities, the signatures of six other princes who were heads of state in six other German provinces also being appended. It was headed, "The Confession of Augsburg."

While the document had been prepared by a group of theologians, inspired by Luther, it was decided that it would have much more weight at the diet if it were presented by the princes and councils of the independent cities since they were not under proscription by the papacy.

The document, translated into Latin, was offered to the diet by one of the Lutheran doctors, Pontanus, who announced before he began to read the paper, "By the grace of God this confession shall prevail, in spite of the gates of hell."

At this same session Martin Bucer, a former Dominican monk who had left the Church in 1521, shortly after Martin Luther had challenged the prelates, offered a similar statement concerning the sentiment of the Swiss Protestants. Bucer had earlier attempted to reconcile the differences between Martin and Zwingli but had been unsuccessful in his endeavor.

Although this was before the emperor had reached Augsburg, some of the most earnest of the clerics who sought to uphold the papal view recommended that the emperor should be urged to put an immediate stop to the dissemination of the opinions of both Protestant groups, since they were so widely at variance with established usage and belief. The diet, therefore, in effect, had been in session before the emperor reached Augsburg since they had considered this piece of business.

The princes who had arrived earlier, as well as the representatives of the free cities, were eager to make some accommodation between the various views in order to keep the empire intact and they, therefore, recommended that a more lenient course than that which had previously been taken should be adopted. But the Catholic princes among them voted to instruct the Romish theologians who were in attendance to draw up a refutation of the articles which had been set forth in the two Evangelical documents. They suggested, however, that those who were to be entrusted with this task should avoid the use of all offensive expressions.

Despite this word of caution, the Catholic theologians decided to attempt to enact a much more belligerent program than previous diets had done. Archbishop Faber of Vienna indicated that he intended to demolish the Swiss confession and set about to do so immediately. The attempt to disprove the Lutheran confession devolved upon Martin's old foe, Eck, with the assistance of an Italian theologian, Cochlaeus.

Seeking to set the stage for Eck's work the Duke of Bavaria, one of the few German nobles who upheld the papal view, asked Eck, "Can you confute that paper out of the Bible?"

134

Eck readily replied, "No. To rebut these statements by Scripture is impossible; but it may easily be done from the fathers."

In making such a statement, Eck came to the very heart of the controversy. The followers of Luther based their authority for the existence of the Church and its sacraments on the Bible and the teachings of Jesus. The papal party, on the other hand, depended upon the traditions which had been built up around the Church and the office of pope throughout the centuries since its founding.

Nevertheless, still awaiting the arrival of the emperor, it was suggested that the two parties should make a further attempt to reconcile their differences. The Protestant statements had made a strong impression upon some of the Roman Catholic members of the diet, especially because they seemed to be so earnestly and honestly presented. Philip Melancthon, representing the Lutheran cause, made every effort to find some common ground of agreement.

The effort was fruitless. The gulf was too wide to be bridged. The conferees reported back to the diet that they had tried in vain to find a common ground from which they could negotiate a settlement.

Meanwhile, Martin was chafing at his confinement, but he was also getting a much needed rest. He did not leave the vicinity of the castle but often strayed out into the countryside, accompanied by several attendants. Generally he dressed in rural costume when he walked through the woods or along a country road.

He made friends of the farmers but refrained from discussing with them any of the questions confronting the diet. Instead he conversed with them about crops and cattle. Often children would join Martin and his friends and he greatly enjoyed their chatter.

Among the books which Martin had taken with him, was a copy of Aesop's Fables. The fanciful character of some of his letters to his dear ones undoubtedly stemmed from his reading of the stories of this ancient writer. Walking through the woods was almost his only recreation aside from reading the tales which Aesop wrote.

He longed for letters from home. Katie wrote as often as she could but family duties made it impossible for her to write as many as she would have desired.

Frequently, instead of writing to Katie, Martin would address an epistle either to young Hans or to his newest child. Katie and

135

Martin had decided that the baby should be named Magdalene. Before her birth they had been so confident that God would send them another daughter, that they had not selected a name for a boy. They had not baptized Magdalene immediately as was the custom, but had decided that Martin should wait until he would return from Coburg.

In every letter home, Martin evidenced his concern for Magdalene's health. He also continually reminded his wife that she should spare herself until she had completely recovered from her experience in bearing the child. Reassured not only by Katie but by the wife of Pastor Bugenhagen, who had also been apprised of Martin's hiding-place, he wrote cheerful letters, but he also confessed to Katie that it was with difficulty that he waited for a sight of his wife and children.

Of Magdalene he wrote, "She must be beautiful indeed by now and probably especially beloved of our Saviour, since she was named for one of whom our Saviour thought so highly."

One letter which Martin wrote to Hans was a mixture of sound advice and whimsey. It read:

> Grace and peace in Christ, dear son. I am glad that you are studying and saying your prayers. Continue to do so, my son, and when I come home I will bring you a pretty present.
>
> I know a lovely, pleasant garden where many children are; they wear golden jackets, and gather nice apples under the trees, and pears and cherries, and purple plums and yellow plums, and sing and run and jump and are happy and have pretty little ponies with golden reins and silver saddles. I asked the man who owned the garden who they were. He said, "They are the children who say their prayers and study and are good." Then said I, "Dear man, I also have a son whose name is Hans Luther; may he come into the garden and eat the sweet apples and pears and ride a fine pony and play with these children?" Then the man said, "If he says his prayers and is good he may come into the garden and Phil and Justy too, and when they all come they shall have whistles and drums and fifes and shall dance and shoot little crossbows."
>
> Then he showed me a fine, large lawn in the garden for dancing, where hung real golden whistles and fine silver crossbows. But it was yet early, and the children had not finished eating, and I could not wait to see them dance. So I said to the man, "My dear sir, I must go and write at once to my dear little Hans about all this, so that he will say his prayers and study and be good, so that he may come into the garden, and he has an Auntie Lena whom

he must bring with him." Then the man said, "All right, go and tell him about it." So, dear little Hans, study and say your prayers, and tell Phil and Justy to say their prayers and study too, so you may all come into the garden together. God bless you. Give Auntie Lena my love and a kiss from me.

Your loving father,
MARTIN LUTHER

Letters such as these alternated with missives to Philip Melancthon who was kept busy at the meeting of the diet. There were those who thought that, because of his mild and conciliatory manner, Philip might be able to accomplish that which the stormy Luther would not be able to achieve. However, Philip, mild-mannered though he was, was just as earnest in his beliefs as was Martin; and the split between the papal party and the Lutherans had reached such a point that no compromise was possible.

Finally the emperor arrived and reviewed the entire situation. He had hoped that a diet which he directed might be able to achieve what previous councils and diets had failed to do, but he discovered that the results of this one had been as unsatisfactory as its predecessors. Angrily he made known to the Lutheran electors that they would have to submit themselves unanimously to the see of Rome and return to the precise forms of worship which had been established in the empire.

Melancthon, seeing the direction in which affairs were now going, wrote a report of the situation to Martin in which he expressed his fears that the cause of Protestantism was losing ground. Still confident of the ultimate success of the Evangelicals, Martin reproved Philip for his unbelief in his reply and added:

> If it be false that God has given His Son for us, then the devil, or whoever you please, may be said to be in my place; but if it be true, what need is there of our care and solicitude, our sadness and trepidation? As though He who gave us His Son, would not help us in these lighter matters; or as though the devil were stronger than He. In private griefs and struggles thou art stronger than I; but in public difficulties the strength is mine.
>
> On the contrary, thou art in public as I am in private; if that should be called private which occurs between Satan and me. Thou fearest nothing for thyself; thou fearest all for the public; while I, for the public cause, am quite at ease, because I know it to be the just and true cause of Christ and God. I am, therefore, a quiet and secure spectator. If we are ruined, God will be ruined with us; Christ the ruler of the world. And let it be so.

Better sink with Christ than reign with Caesar. I beseech thee by Christ, that thou neglect not those promises and consolations of which the Psalms and Evangelists are full. Cast thy care upon God; wait upon the Lord, be of good courage, and He shall strengthen thine heart. "Be of good cheer," said Christ, "I have overcome the world." If the world be conquered, shall we fear it as though it were victor? This is not good: I know it is weakness of faith. Let us pray, with the apostles, "Lord, increase our faith."

Philip's fears that the conference would decide against the Lutherans were, however, well-founded. The final decision which was actually not approved until most of the Evangelical members had retired from the city, was an outright victory for the papal party. All rebellion against the papacy or any of its decrees and decisions must cease. The churches were all instructed to return to the use of the Roman ritual for all services: the priests were ordered to pledge their allegiance once more to the Church.

14

THE Elector John stopped at Coburn on his way back to his home in Saxony and reported to Martin Luther on the results of the Diet of Augsburg.

"I suppose that I was suspected of disloyalty to our brethren when I carried the Sword of State in the Corpus Christi procession," John said. "Some of them doubtless assumed that I had left the cause of Protestantism because I sought to be conciliatory. But I thought that there was a possibility that some kind of compromise might be devised by which we might have various forms of worship within the Church. By riding with the emperor I thought to indicate that, though we had a quarrel with the Church, we Protestants were loyal to him."

"But it was to no avail," he continued. "Philip Melancthon worked with me to ascertain if such a plan could be arranged, but the papal delegates would not yield an inch. I left the conference with the conviction that not only was the Church about to be rent asunder but that the empire might share in such a fate."

"Where did the emperor stand then on the propositions which you and Philip submitted?" Martin inquired. "At previous meetings I seemed to detect a conciliatory attitude on his part. Has his attitude changed?"

"Definitely," John replied. "Since he made his peace with the pope he has gone over completely to the side of the papacy. He now seems to assume that the pope and his prelates can do no wrong."

Luther bowed his head in thought. He had still dared to hope that the Church would not be divided once more as it had been in the past when there had been the separation between the East and West. Christ's body should not be divided. Paul had said that there were many different members in one body and that, while each member had different functions, the body was still one.

Could not the Church be like that? Could there not be some who, while loyal to Jesus Christ, would yet worship Him in different ways from the manner in which others paid Him homage? Apparently this was not to be. He sighed deeply.

"What, then, is the next step to be?" he inquired.

"We will probably be forced to form a confederation of Protestant princes," John asserted. "The emperor may attempt to punish all who will not acknowledge the supremacy of Rome. If he takes such action we must be ready to resist."

There was further discussion of the attitudes of individual princes.

"They showed a most conciliatory disposition. They are truly loyal to the emperor," John said, "but when they are faced with the necessity to choose between Christ and the empire they will choose Christ."

"And now, sire, is there need for me to stay here longer?" Martin inquired. "Unless your Excellency should desire to have me do so, I would like to return to my family. Just before I came here, Sire, a new babe was born to Katie."

"Wonderful!" John exclaimed.

Impulsively the elector reached into his purse.

"Here! Give the child this with my blessing," he said.

Into Martin's hand fell ten gold pieces.

"Sire, you are too good," Martin ejaculated.

Soon afterward Martin packed up his clothing, his books, and his lute and set out for Wittenberg, accompanied by his two secretaries and some of the attendants who had been with him in the castle.

Martin decided not to inform Katie of his projected arrival in order that he might surprise his family. After an uneventful journey homeward he arrived at midday, still attired in the clothing which he wore when he took his walks in the countryside near the castle.

Young Hans was the first to see him as Martin's conveyance drew up in front of the former monastery. For a moment he looked at Martin uncertainly. Then his face lighted and he threw himself impulsively into his father's arms.

"*Vater! Vater!*" he shouted joyfully.

Katie came running out to the entry and embraced Martin warmly. Tears streamed down her cheeks as she murmured, "Thank God!"

Martin took a huge handkerchief out of the pocket of his cloak and wiped her eyes tenderly although there were tears in his own which persisted in cascading down his cheeks. Hans reached up his chubby arms to be taken and Martin soon was hugging mother and son with rough affection.

"The baby?" Martin questioned. "How is she?"

"You must see how she has grown," Katie said proudly. "She is indeed a healthy infant."

Martin started impulsively for the nursery and then turned to Katie. "Oh, but I am forgetting," he ejaculated. "First I want you to meet the fine men who were with me at Coburg Castle. And do we have enough food in the larder to invite them to dine with us?"

"Of course," Katie replied.

Martin presented his friends who, somewhat sheepishly, shook hands with Katie. She kissed Martin's two secretaries on their ruddy cheeks and insisted that they remain, with Martin's escorts, for dinner.

"And thank you for looking after my Dr. Luther," she exclaimed.

"And now, if you'll excuse me, my friends, I must see the baby who was born just before I went to Coburg. Take seats about the fireplace and make yourselves at home."

When Martin tiptoed into the nursery, Magdalene was sleeping soundly. Her chubby cheeks were a deep shade of pink and Martin looked down at the child with adoring eyes. Hans came rushing into the room and inadvertently bumped into the cradle. The baby awoke, yawned, rubbed her eyes, and then stretched out her arms. She smiled up at Martin although she was undoubtedly unaware of who or what was in the room. She was only conscious of the fact that there was some activity around her.

"Look!" Martin exclaimed to Katie. "She recognizes me."

"You have much to learn about babies still," Katie chided. "Babies as young as Magda recognize no one by sight. They really know only the one who feeds them."

"I am positive . . ."

"You are always positive," Katie interrupted, smiling, "but

141

that does not alter facts. Come now; dinner is ready and we must not keep our guests waiting."

Within minutes callers came to greet Martin, interrupting the dinner hour. Among the first was Philip.

"Welcome home, Dr. Luther!" he exclaimed. "We rejoice that we can all be together again. I am only sorry that I could not bring you good news from the meeting of the diet."

"Philip, you have really brought me the best tidings possible," Martin protested. "Now we know where we stand. Reunion with Rome is impossible. That is now altogether apparent. As matters stand, we must establish the Evangelical Church so that it will be the Church Universal for Germany. While we should never close the door upon the Roman Church, neither should we depart one ell from the faith which we hold. We had best forget the pope now and build a Church whose foundation shall be acknowledged to be Christ, the Son of God, and whose guidebook is the Holy Bible."

"You have always been so zealous to reform the Church, Martin. I am now interested to observe that you have decided that it cannot be done, that we must build anew," Philip remarked.

"Look you, Philip, do you not feel that this is the only thing that we can do?" Martin asked.

"I do indeed."

Nor were these two the only ones who felt thus. The Protestant princes decided that they would have to form a league for the protection and preservation of their faith. Martin had opposed any such defensive alliance heretofore, hoping always that a reconciliation could be effected and also convinced that he owed allegiance to the temporal government of Charles and the Holy Roman Empire.

In effect he agreed to forswear such allegiance and cast in his lot with those who were ready to partition the empire.

The following year he published two lengthy pamphlets in which he asserted that it was the duty of Christians to resist such attacks as those which were initiated by the edict of Augsburg. He added that it was the solemn and imperative duty of the reformed sovereigns to prepare to defend their lands from any incursion which came from outside of Germany.

The lawyers of Saxony reinforced Luther's stand by publishing their own pamphlet in which they declared that the emperor had usurped a jurisdiction in matters which were solely ecclesiastical

142

in making a decree which the temporal ruler had promulgated at the Diet of Augsburg. He had threatened an infraction of the independence and internal freedom of the several provinces which had acknowledged the validity of the Protestant faith.

Basing his action upon Luther's pamphlets and the action of the Saxon lawyers, Philip, the landgrave of Hesse, always impulsive, formed a defensive alliance with the imperial city of Strasburg and with the Swiss cantons of Basel and Zurich.

A few months later, at the initiation of the landgrave, a meeting of the Evangelical rulers occurred in which a treaty was formulated guaranteeing mutual aid in the event of attack by forces outside of the area. This was to result less than a year later in the formation of an organization known as the League of Smalcalde.

The famous pact of Smalcalde contained the promise from each of the contracting powers to maintain a standing army for mutual defense for the ensuing six years. It was a treaty which bound all of the cities and provinces signing it to come to the defense of one or more of the other parties in the event that the emperor started an aggressive war against one or more of them. In effect, although the princes and representatives of the cities who signed the pact were indicating that they had thereby severed all their ties with the emperor, they actually regarded their action as merely defensive.

At the same time that they initialed the pact, they signed a manifesto in which they demanded that a free and general council of the Church should be convened, that prior to such a council, the Church should purge itself of all practices which they regarded as contrary to sound religion. They further resolutely denied that the emperor had any authority in the field of religion, and explained why they regarded as necessary the formation of such a compact.

Charles was justifiably alarmed at this indication of rebellion against his authority. His advisers had assured him that he could subdue the reformers by threats and overt acts against them and this now seemed to be impossible. He was further concerned when he received word that the League had opened negotiations with Francis I of France and Henry VIII of England, looking toward a defensive pact with those countries.

He had cause to regret the fact that he had so recently held Francis in captivity. Upon his release that monarch had formed an alliance with Henry VIII which alliance was now being strengthened by the pacts which the two had formed with the Smalcaldic League.

These political trends actually gave Martin and the reformers in Europe a period of comparative peace. Martin became more than a reformer: he became the living symbol of reform. For this reason he continued to dwell in comparative safety. Much as the emperor had come to hate and despise him, he realized that if he were to arrange for the assassination of the former German monk, he would plunge the empire into a war which quite conceivably might be lost.

The emperor had a strong army, to be sure, but he was not certain of the loyalty of all his commanders and their legions. The balance of power quite possibly might be on the side of those who supported Martin Luther.

Unaware, in reality, of the political tugging and pulling which was happening around him, Martin continued with his work, teaching in the university, occasionally conducting the services in the parish church, caring for his family. More than ever before scholars flocked to Wittenberg to listen to his lectures and sit in his classes.

He was undoubtedly the greatest expositor of Scriptures since Augustine, and to his classes came scholars who adhered to the Reformed faith but were not Lutheran in their theology. Among such were followers of John Calvin and Ulrich Zwingli, and even students from England. Now in his late forties, Martin was at the height of his power as a teacher.

He traveled frequently, lecturing at other universities and preaching in other pulpits than that of the parish church in Wittenberg.

"Do you have to spend so much time away from home?" Katie wistfully inquired one day. "Philip Melancthon rarely leaves Wittenberg, Pastor Bugenhagen less often than he."

"I wish that I could spend all my time here," Martin assured her, "especially in the winter-time; but it is hard to refuse these invitations to speak in other centers of our country. The requests arrive constantly, however, and I cannot well refuse them. You see, my dear, people identify a movement with a man. Although I have constantly sought to explain to our people that this is an Evangelical Reformation — that is, one which is based upon the teachings of the Scriptures — they still speak of it as the 'Lutheran reformation' as if it were mine."

144

"Well, but can't you reform the churches from right here in Wittenberg?" Katie objected.

Martin laughed.

"Would that I could or that someone else could take my place back of a pulpit. They still insist that Martin Luther must come," Martin explained. "But, Katie, dear, I am trying to indoctrinate others so that they can take my place. I'm not as young as I was when the reformation began, you know."

"Nonsense," she objected. "You are not old. You are the father of little children. That would be impossible if you were an old man."

"But I was a middle-aged man before I knew what it was to be a father," Martin retorted.

Both were well-content then when a lull came in the calls for Martin's service outside of Wittenberg. The empire was threatened once more, and Charles, alarmed at the division which had occurred, sought to arrange at least a temporary truce. The Turks were still marching westward and Charles was fearful that Solyman and his hordes of Moslems would overrun all of western Europe. For this reason, the emperor sought the intervention of the elector palatine and the archbishop of Mentz to intercede with the members of the Smalcaldic League.

In July, 1531, members of the League and representatives of the emperor signed a treaty of pacification in Nuremberg. The following month, the members who had failed to attend, held another consultation and ratified the agreement at Ratisbon. According to the terms of the agreement, the Protestants were permitted to use their own ceremonials in their worship services and to profess and practice the Reformed doctrine. The decrees of Worms and Augsburg were abrogated.

It was further stipulated that a council would be assembled within six months to settle upon a rule of faith acceptable to people and clergy in all parts of the empire. The Protestant princes, on their part, agreed to aid in the prosecution of the war against the Turks and to confirm the archduke of Austria as Roman emperor.

But the pope was highly incensed at the emperor once more. He had hoped that the empire might proceed against the Protestant princes and particularly against Martin Luther, anticipating that his adherents would silence Luther once and forever, little realizing, perhaps, that the death of Luther would not have stopped the progress of the Reformation. While Martin was the undisputed leader of the Protestant movement in Germany, there would have been others to take his place if he had been removed.

Nor were all of the Protestants happy about the truce.

Dr. Bugenhagen protested to Martin, "Whenever we make an agreement to postpone a final decision, we weaken our cause."

"No, no, pastor," Martin replied. "We strengthen it, and we certainly do not want to have a war in which Christian would be pitted against Christian."

"You do not call the pope, Christian, do you?" Bugenhagen retorted.

Martin smiled.

"I have called him many things, good friend," Martin explained. "In some respects he has been on the side of Satan but he, like most of us, has a battleground in his own soul. There are times when Christ is regnant, and other times when Satan rules. There must be room within the Church Catholic for many forms of worship, for many groups of Christians."

Martin, therefore, let it be known that he favored the agreement. He was well aware of what a catastrophe it would be for all Christendom if the Turks were to push their way to the Atlantic Ocean.

The agreement had scarcely been ratified when news came that Solyman, with three hundred thousand men, had invaded Hungary. Charles went out to the battlefield himself, leading his own troops and those supplied by the Protestant princes. Before they could engage the Turks in battle, however, the latter withdrew eastward and the immediate threat of invasion was thwarted.

In the same month John, the great elector of Saxony, died. He was succeeded by his son, John Frederick, who lacked many of the sterling qualities of his father but was still a loyal Protestant. He soon discovered that the emperor would observe the terms of the compact with the members of the Smalcaldic League only when it suited his convenience to do so. For this reason the elector leaned heavily upon Martin for advice in matters of faith.

He was not without courage and daring to uphold the Protestant cause but he had little knowledge of the basic tenents of the Protestant faith. Nevertheless he earnestly sought to advance the ideals and purposes of the two great electors for whom he had been named.

On November 7th, 1531, another son was born to Katie and Martin.

146

As soon after the babe was delivered, as Martin was permitted by the midwife to enter Katie's chamber, Martin asked his wife, "Have you considered the name which we should give to the child?"

"I have," she acknowledged.

"Then I hope that your choice agrees with my own," Martin said.

"What would you call him?" Katie asked.

"Philip," Martin replied. "I know that my good comrade Philip would be overjoyed to have one of our children named for him. Certainly he has been our most loyal friend and associate through all the years that I have known him."

"Splendid idea, Dr. Luther, and I would agree save for one thing," Katie suggested tactfully. "Our first child was named Hans for his two grandfathers. It is time now that one of our children should be named for his father."

"Oh, no," Martin objected.

"Oh, yes," Katie countered.

"We will think about it," Martin conceded.

Katie reinforced her decision with an appeal to Philip.

"Like Martin, I should like to have one of our little ones bear your name," she announced to Philip, "but I feel that this son should be named for his father. Do you not also consider that he should be called for Dr. Luther?"

"I most certainly do," Philip asserted positively, emphatically nodding his head in agreement. "I will speak to Dr. Luther about it."

At their weekly conference Philip broached the subject to his friend. They had had their usual discussion concerning both theological subjects and political trends in the empire.

Philip expressed his appreciation for Martin's desire to compliment him by naming the child for him. "But *Frau* Luther is right," he insisted. "One of your sons should be named for you."

"You have been talking to her then?" Martin countered accusingly.

"I have," Philip acknowledged. "And she is deeply concerned about the matter."

"But she really doesn't understand my feeling," Martin protested. "You have truly been as a son or a younger brother to me; and I should like to have one of my children bear your beloved name."

"Then why not name your next boy for me?" Philip suggested. "You named the firstborn for your and Katie's fathers — Hans — and that was fitting and appropriate. The next son most certainly should be called Martin. But the third son could be called Philip if you so desired."

"Very well then," Martin agreed reluctantly, "but you must be the one to baptize the babe."

"Gladly, good doctor," Philip acquiesced, "and at your convenience."

On the Sunday when Martin next occupied the pulpit of the Wittenberg church, therefore, Philip Melancthon baptized little Martin.

"He will be a great man like his father," Katie proudly asserted.

15

IN 1534 a new pope was elected who chose to be called Paul III. Whenever, after Martin had fired the opening shot of the Reformation by nailing his theses to the door of the Wittenberg church, a new pope was chosen, he had eagerly waited to see whether the long hoped for change in papal thinking would occur. By this time, however, Martin had given up anticipating that a reformation in the Church would occur.

When Philip heard of the election of the new pope, he naively and wistfully inquired of Martin, "Do you suppose that Pope Paul will make any attempt to reform the Church, do away with indulgences, and seek to ameliorate the lot of the poor peasants of the world?"

"That is what I have continued to pray and hope might happen," Martin replied, "but I have long since given up any expectation of reform from within. There is now established in the world — not only in Germany, England, Scotland, France, the low countries, but even in Italy — a body of Christians who are concerned to interpret the mind of Christ and the will of God for the world — but they are not in the Roman Church. And whoever the pope may be, he will continue to fight reform.

"The Evangelical churches in those countries are not perfect, although we who have cast in our lot with them still strive for perfection, and we certainly lay no claim to infallibility. Certainly Martin Luther is not infallible, and Zwingli, although I have frequently disagreed with his stubborn attitude, does not claim to be infallible. So we shall continue to make mistakes, continue to sin — —you, I, Ulrich Zwingli, John Calvin and the others. We shall commit errors, but none of us claim that we alone are in possession of the truth. No, I must admit that I no longer have any desire to return to Rome where one man claims that he alone speaks for Almighty God."

If Pope Paul earnestly sought to reform the Church — and this had been his declared intention — he found himself thwarted by the prelates who had discovered that a constant source of income for themselves and for their various projects lay in the system of indulgences which they had established, and so he, too, gradually acceded to their wishes.

Pope Paul did, nevertheless, make one more effort to bring Luther back into the fold. He promised that a council would be called to consider Martin's case and he sent a papal nuncio to confer with Martin. The papal representative was instructed to secure Martin's consent to attend such a council and even to choose among several cities where such a council could be held.

Cardinal Verger, the papal nuncio, seems to have been a man of considerable ability and apparently he was able to win at least a sympathetic audience with Martin. However, having been disappointed and cavilly treated so often, Martin frankly opposed the calling of a council to discuss his case.

"It is now useless to hold such a meeting," Martin told the papal legate. "If the pope should call a council, the delegates would allow no matter of importance to come before it; nothing would be accomplished by it. What would the council consider? Tonsures and robes, and trivial matters of that sort, would be all that its members would consider, instead of the great issues of justification, faith and Christian unity. In matters of doctrine I, and those who think with me, had no need of any light that a council could afford it.

"Our opinions are fixed: and the only value of a council would be to settle the beliefs of persons who are ignorant and weak enough to take their notions from other men. Nevertheless, if a council really is to be assembled and I am invited, I would attend, even though I should know beforehand that it would surely send me to the flames."

Unlike the other papal representatives who had previously conferred with Martin, Verger took no offense at his remarks. Mildly he inquired, "Where would you prefer that this council should be held?"

Readily Martin responded, "Anywhere you please. Let it be at Patavia, Florence or Mantau, or wherever else you choose: it is indifferent to me. In whatever place it may convene I will be there."

"Suppose that the pope should visit you in Wittenberg," suggested Verger tentatively.

"Let him come by all means," Martin said cordially. Then he added, "But would you have him come alone or with an army at his back?"

"Would you object if he should come with a guard only sufficiently large enough to protect him?" Verger continued.

"As he will," Martin responded indifferently. "With a guard or with an army. It is immaterial to me. In either case we will be ready for him."

As the conference between the two came to a close the papal nuncio said, "Do not forget, Doctor, to be in readiness for the council."

The humorous smile which accompanied Verger's words took the sting from them.

"Have no fear, my Lord Bishop," Martin responded, also smiling. "Depend upon it, I will be present at the council, though I know it will be at the risk of my neck."

Having secured the acquiescence of Martin, Verger went on to confer with the elector John Frederick and Prince Philip of Hesse. He reported to them that Martin had consented to attend a meeting of the council wherever it should be held.

"My father and uncle bequeathed to me the task of protecting that noble man, Martin Luther," John Frederick announced coldly. "I can assure your grace that I shall never allow him to attend a meeting or a council with the representatives of the papacy, or the pope himself, outside of the area over which I exert control or a province which is governed by my friend, Prince Philip. We have had too many vain promises to place much faith in the person, whoever he may be, who is the incumbent of the papal throne."

"Suppose that the pope himself were to come to Germany. If he were to convene a council in Saxony would you guarantee him safe conduct?" Verger asked.

"Of course," the elector assured him, "but make no mistake about it. He will not come."

"Do not be too confident of that," Verger countered.

But John Frederick was right. When the papal nuncio returned to Rome and made his report, suggesting that it might be advantageous to hold a council in Germany the pope said, "Absurd. I cannot go to the beggar monk. He must come to me."

Even if he had been so minded, however, Pope Paul would have been dissuaded from going because of a new development. His predecessor a few years before had conferred upon Henry VIII of England the title of "Defender of the Faith," but Henry had tired of his wife, Catherine of Aragon, the aunt of Emperor Charles V, and had asked the pope to free him from the conjugal vows which he had made.

Because of Catherine's relationship to Charles, the pope hesitated to take this step and finally issued an outright refusal. Henry forthwith announced that he repudiated all allegiance to the pope and further declared that the English clergy thereafter would be under his authority and not that of the pope.

All thought of a conference or council was put aside for the moment. The empire, as well as the papacy, was in danger, and the climate for a successful council would be most unpropitious.

At this time, in order to shore up his own defenses, Henry petitioned the princes of the Smalcaldic League for an alliance promising mutual protection. The princes eagerly accepted the proposal but, having in mind the fact that the pope had once conferred upon Henry the title of "Defender of the Faith," they added the proviso that he would have to agree to promote the adoption in England of the precepts embodied in the Confession of Augsburg. He would probably have done so had he not ascertained that the princes had no intention of dispatching troops to England in case the island was attacked by the forces of Emperor Charles. For this reason, after long negotiations, no treaty was signed.

One result of the negotiations, however, which were conducted by the bishop of Hereford and several other clergymen with members of the Smalcaldic League, was that these English clergymen became thoroughly indoctrinated with the principles of the Reformation since, after they had held their conferences with the princes, they spent some time in Wittenberg. They brought back from Germany the spiritual basis of the Reformation, its theology, and a new point of view regarding the authority of the Scriptures as the basis upon which the Church and its sacraments should rest.

At approximately the same time that the League and representatives of the British crown were seeking to find a basis for a mutual defense pact, a Concord of Wittenberg was being drawn up by representatives of the Swiss Protestants and the followers of Luther. Ulrich Zwingli was not present with the representatives since he had been killed in 1531. He had been serving at the time as chaplain of the Zurich forces which had been fighting the five forest cantons which had not accepted the principles of church reform. He was killed in the battle of Kappel, October 11, 1531. When Martin had heard the news of Zwingli's death he had immediately written to the Reformed group in Switzerland to express his deep sympathy for their loss.

The Concord recognized the different positions which each group held regarding the eucharist, but noted that in all other matters they were united. As a result of the Concord, the Protestant towns in Switzerland were permitted to merge with the Smalcaldic League in planning for their mutual defense. The League had continued to grow during the years which had elapsed since its founding.

Another child was born to Katie early in 1533. Martin and Katie had agreed when young Martin was born that the next child, if he were a boy, should be called Philip, but both apparently forgot the decision or set it aside and, instead, named the boy for the apostle whose letters and writings had been the foundation stone upon which Luther's theology rested, Paul, the great missionary apostle.

Martin had never been robust since his university days. He was a hearty eater and, in consequence, suffered numerous digestive disorders. Scarcely a winter passed without his being afflicted with some respiratory ailment. Now in his fifties, therefore, he was often confined to his bed due to illness. Nevertheless, however incapacitated he might be, he always seemed able to respond to calls for his service in churches or universities.

He spent as much time as possible with his children, concerned not only to indoctrinate his family with the basic principles of the Reformation but to inculcate in them other precepts related to daily living. Back of the huge tiled stove in the great hall of their home, he posted a series of maxims which he encouraged his children to memorize in the hope that they would become bases upon which they would build their lives.

They seemed to have been chosen at random from rules which he had heard from others, and which he himself had composed. The list was as follows:

"Whoso is faithful in little things will also be faithful in great things and who is unfaithful in little things will be un-righteous in great things.

"Who is diligent in little things will be diligent in much.
"Who esteems not a penny will never have a *gulden*.
"Who wastes an hour will waste a day.
"Who despises the small will never get the large.
"Who despises the gizzard will not get the hen.
"Who will not learn his letters will never learn anything.
"Who cannot live on a hundred *gulden* cannot live on a thousand."

Martin was eager to have his children secure their education without facing the struggles through which he passed in his youth. He was not opposed to the idea that his children should learn to work and he assigned home tasks with the firmness of a stern disciplinarian. The children could never retire for the evening until every task which had been assigned them had been completed, but he was eager to see that no task interfered with their learning.

"Learning is a task too," he explained to Katie. "As it has been my task to lecture and teach in the university, so is it theirs to learn in the schools to which they are sent. If they should have to earn a living at the same time that they are learning, they might miss out on some of the most important truths which they require in order to learn how to live."

Margaret was born in 1534. By this time Hans was of great assistance to his parents in caring for the children who were younger than he. Katie was glad to entrust the older children to him while she looked after the babies herself.

"He is better than any nursemaid," she told Martin.

But Martin was fearful that his son might become effeminate although he did not confide his misgivings to Katie.

"It is good that he is interested in the younger ones," he remarked, "but we must take care to see that he plays and works with other boys his own age."

"He does that too. Never fear," she reassured her husband.

"Good."

In 1538 Christian III, King of Denmark, brought his country into the Smalcaldic League. "These Norsemen are sturdy," Martin told Pastor Bugenhagen. "If they have accepted our Evangelical faith they will prove staunch allies."

"Yes," Bugenhagen agreed, "but do they understand what it means to be Evangelical? One day they are Roman Catholic.

The next day the king says, 'Now we are Evangelical,' but do they know what it means to become such?"

"Probably not," Luther replied, "but since the country is now open to the proclamation of our faith, we can send some of our best scholars to Denmark as well as some of our finest young men who are preparing for the Christian ministry. The scholars can indoctrinate the priests: the young men can speak to the people. And the fact is, Pastor, that many of them have long been ready for this. They have been sending many young men to Wittenberg to attend my lectures. What has happened has been that the king and his court have long been sympathetic to our cause, but until they allied themselves with the League they did not dare to make an open profession of their belief."

There were also losses, however. Not all of Saxony adhered to the government of the elector. There was a sizable group of people who gave their allegiance to Duke George, and the duke was an avowed enemy of the Reformation. He had been constantly pressing the emperor to send troops into Saxony to take over the province and depose the elector. The emperor wisely refrained from doing so. He realized, if the duke did not, that if he had followed Duke George's suggestion, all of Protestant Germany would have sprung to the defense of the elector.

But George's sudden death changed the picture. George was succeeded by his brother Henry who was a staunch Protestant and a friend of the elector. In the area over which he governed, Duke Henry set about to integrate the province with Protestant Saxony and with the other German states which were allied with the Reformation. And many of the local priests had long entertained secret longings to join the Protestant cause, and now very eagerly joined the movement.

In 1539 a solemn festival was held in Leipzig which was jointly sponsored by the elector and the duke. Protestantism was officially declared to be the religion of the province.

Because of recurring illnesses, Martin rarely left Wittenberg anymore. It fell upon Philip Melancthon to represent him at conferences and various other gatherings. Frail though Philip appeared to be, he was actually indefatigable. His slight frame was as misleading as his calm manner of speaking. He seemed to be more willing to compromise than was Martin but, in truth, he was as inflexible in standing for what he regarded essential as was Martin.

Martin's principal disorder during his later years was diagnosed as "the stone," which today would be known as an infection of the gall bladder. He would occasionally be stricken right in the middle of a lecture. Various treatments were prescribed for him but none were successful. For a time hot and cold packs, alternately applied, seemed to help him avert the most intense pain.

However, he still insisted upon serving whenever he was called for some special assignment. Thus, in 1546, when the counts of Mansfeld began to dispute with one another in respect to certain property rights which each claimed and they decided to invite Martin to adjudicate their differences, Martin repaired at once to their home in the town of Eisleben where he had been born. Martin had no presentiment, when he said good-by to Katie and his children as he set out on his journey, that he would not see his family again.

Affectionately he put his arm around Hans. "You are my sturdy son," he said. "While I am gone you will look after your mother and the family, won't you?"

"I will, Father. I will," Hans assured him.

"And I'll come home as soon as I can," Martin said with a smile, "but it may take some time for me to get those two quarreling counts together."

It was a remarkable tribute to the character of Martin that the two noblemen had chosen him who, had he not entered the university and later the priesthood, would have been one of their vassals, to adjudicate their differences.

When Martin reached Eisleben he was met by two counts with a retinue of a hundred horsemen. They escorted him to lodgings which had been set aside for his use during his sojourn in the city. The entire populace of Eisleben cheered him as he passed through the streets.

Martin would have plunged immediately into the task of reconciling the two noblemen, but the journey, in the dead of winter, had proved too much for him. He came down with a severe fever which caused him to be confined to his bed for several days. Then, eager to be about his task, he left his bed before the fever abated and sought to begin his work.

He went to the hall where the meeting with the two counts was to take place but, after several days of exhausting conferences, the effort proved to be too much for him, and on the 16th of Feb-

156

ruary he had to take to his bed again, stricken with a severe congestion of the lungs.

Colius, the Protestant minister of the Eisleben church, called upon him and sought to cheer him, but Martin had succumbed once more to a period of despondency.

Martin remarked to Colius, "Here I was born and baptized: what if I should remain to die here also?"

"Do not talk of death, dear friend," Colius remonstrated. "You have work to do here, and the Lord would not terminate your life until that task was accomplished."

However, on the 17th, Martin took a turn for the worse. His hosts summoned Count Albert of Mansfeld, together with two physicians. The latter shook their heads when Albert looked into their faces for confirmation of his hopes that Martin would recover.

Martin had had many premonitions of death before, but on this occasion he had more than a premonition. He was certain that he would die.

"Will you kneel, Sire," he asked the count, "while I make my peace with God?"

The count dropped to his knees as did the two doctors and Martin's attendants. Then, in a husky voice, Martin prayed: "O my heavenly Father, God of our Lord Jesus Christ, the Father of all consolation, I thank Thee for having revealed to me Thy well-beloved Son, in whom I trust, whom I have acknowledged, and preached, and loved; but whom the pope, and they who have no religion, persecute and oppose. To Thee, O Jesus Christ, I commend my soul. I am casting off this earthly body, and passing from this life; but I know that with Thee I shall abide eternally."

Martin paused for a moment to catch his breath and then recited the words of the Psalmist, echoed by Christ when He was dying on the cross, "Into Thy hands I commend my spirit."

Colius, convinced now that Martin was nearing the final moments of his life, asked him one question: "Dearest father, do you verily confess Jesus Christ, the Son of God, our Saviour and Redeemer?"

Making a final effort to speak Martin faintly replied, "Yes. I do."

Moments later the end came. Martin was then only sixty-two years of age according to the reckoning of the calendar, but so full had been his life, he had been so much in the center of controversy, that he appeared to be much older. And, as evidenced by the words of his prayer, he was still engaged in a struggle with the pope almost up to the moment of his passing.

One final task was finished, however. The counts of Mansfeld felt deeply contrite that they had been the unwitting cause of his demise and they effected a reconciliation before his bier in the Church of St. Andrew in Eisleben where for two days, Martin's body lay in state. The counts immediately notified the elector of Saxony of Martin's death and petitioned him that Martin's remains should be interred in the church there.

"Here he was born and here he should be buried," they said.

However, the elector was otherwise minded.

"His family resides in Wittenberg," the elector said. "There Dr. Luther spent most of his life and he should be interred there."

On February twentieth, a cavalcade left Eisleben for Wittenberg. Nobles from the surrounding area, the elector, the counts of Mansfeld, and a whole host of ordinary citizens followed the coach in which Martin's body had been placed. A courier had been dispatched earlier for Wittenberg.

"Go and tell Dr. Philip Melancthon of Dr. Luther's passing," Count Albert instructed him. "And ask Dr. Melancthon to inform *Frau* Luther of the passing of our friend. He was Dr. Luther's closest friend and will be the one who can best break the sad news to the family."

This was done and upon Philip fell the sad task of informing the widow of her husband's death.

When Philip knocked at the door and Katie appeared in response to his summons, she could tell in an instant that something untoward had happened. Philip's face was so drawn, his eyes were so sad, that she sensed the purport of his visit.

"Something has happened to Martin," she said. "He is ill? Dead?"

"No, dear *Frau* Luther," Philip replied. "He is neither sick nor dead. He has only departed this life to live in eternity with his Father. You remember that our Lord Jesus said, 'I am the resurrection, and the life: he that believeth in me, though he were dead, yet shall he live: and whosoever believeth in me shall never die.' Martin has merely gone on to do a greater work in company with his Lord than he could ever do here."

"The Lord's will be done," Katie murmured.

158

Philip then informed her that Martin's body was on its way from Eisleben, escorted by a company of nobles and friends.

"When will they be here?" she inquired.

"Tomorrow in all probability," he informed her.

"Then we must make ready," she replied, her practical, house-wifely instincts immediately aroused despite her loss, "and we shall have to prepare a meal for these good friends who have provided his escort."

"I'm afraid that will be impossible," Philip said. "Half of the population of Eisleben is coming, according to the courier."

Actually this was an exaggeration. Many people accompanied the cortege out of Eisleben but by the time the procession reached Wittenberg the majority had returned to their homes. However, it was still a large procession which finally reached the barrier of the city. Awaiting the arrival of the funeral procession were town officials, professors and students from the university, Philip and Johann Bugenhagen.

The body of Luther was taken to the cathedral where, after the open casket was displayed for another day to the many who wanted to pay their respects to the Reformation leader, the funeral service took place.

Philip Melancthon delivered the oration which was customary on the occasion of the death of a notable person, ending with the statement, "This simple man of God will be known and remembered throughout the centuries to come as the one who gave the Church back to Christ, its founder, and to the people for whom He died."

Martin's body was interred in the cathedral.

"A mighty fortress is our God, a bulwark never failing," Philip whispered softly to Katie as the body of the reformer was lowered between the flagstones of the central aisle. "Our Dr. Luther is now where no one any longer can threaten or injure him. He has fought the good fight, finished the course, kept the faith. The Lord has laid up for him the winner's crown."